Tales from a

Tales from a
BONDi
v e t

DR CHRIS BROWN
with ANNA HILLE

hachette
AUSTRALIA

Tales from a Bondi Vet is based on the Network Ten series
Bondi Vet produced by WTFN Entertainment Pty Ltd.
Bondi Vet is produced in association with Network Ten.
Created by Daryl Talbot and Steve Oemcke.

hachette
AUSTRALIA

Published in Australia and New Zealand in 2009
by Hachette Australia
(An imprint of Hachette Australia Pty Limited)
Level 17, 207 Kent Street, Sydney NSW 2000
www.hachette.com.au

Cataloguing-in-Publication data available
from the National Library of Australia

ISBN 978 0 7336 2392 9

Cover design by Christabella Designs
Text design by Bookhouse, Sydney
Typeset in 12/17.5 pt Adobe Garamond Pro
Printed in Australia by Griffin Press, Adelaide
All photographs courtesy WTFN Entertainment and Dr Chris Brown
with the exception of the peregrine falcons courtesy James Hutton

Hachette Australia's policy is to use papers
that are natural, renewable and recyclable products
and made from wood grown in sustainable forests.
The logging and manufacturing processes are expected
to conform to the environmental regulations
of the country of origin.

To the creatures and the characters that make working along this piece of coastline so interesting and entertaining

Contents

No Promises

A day in the life of a vet is never predictable. It doesn't matter where you are, in a country practice or, like me, by the sea at Bondi, you never know what situation you are going to find yourself dealing with. And just when you think it is going to be a quiet shift . . .

As soon as I walk into the waiting room and take one look at Zenna, a three-year-old Rottweiler, I know instantly that she is critically ill. Her eyes are wild and she is convulsing. It is difficult to see such a beautiful dog so distressed, but I have to put any emotion aside and do my job. The man with her is panicking and has no idea what to do; he and Zenna are depending on me. But already he has made the right decision in bringing her to the clinic. Immediately, we carry her into the emergency room and I get to work.

Part of trying to find out what is wrong with an animal is asking questions, if you can, of an owner. In this case, it turns out that Gareth, the man who's brought her in, isn't her owner; he's looking after her for his flatmate, Paul. I try to get as much background as I can from Gareth to help me, because I know that I don't have much time. It seems Gareth had come home to find Zenna in this state. He has no idea what is going on.

In my head I run through a list of what may be causing the symptoms I am seeing. None of them are to be taken lightly. It could be something neurological like a seizure or epilepsy, but this is rare in a young dog – and Gareth tells me Zenna has no history of those conditions – so I rule them out pretty quickly.

In the short time Zenna has been with me she has deteriorated further. Her symptoms are definitely not abating. She has diarrhoea, she is tremoring and her temperature has gone up, all signs that suggest to me her body is quite possibly trying to expel something toxic. Her rising temperature is of particular concern – if it goes up too high for a prolonged period, she may suffer brain damage. A case that appeared very serious at the start is now rapidly escalating into one of life or death. I need to get Zenna's temperature down, fast. And, in order to do that, I need to treat the cause of these symptoms, not just the symptoms themselves.

The whole time I have been treating Zenna I have been working through the possible source of her illness. I have concluded that the cause is something fast-acting and potent;

something that can cause a dog's body systems to shut down . . .

'Mate, is there a chance she's been poisoned?' I ask Gareth.

To me this is what it looks like – in addition to the sudden onset of very severe symptoms, Zenna is distressed and confused.

Gareth tells me that Paul – who, as it turns out, is a police officer – has had ongoing problems with a neighbour complaining about Zenna's barking. My heart sinks when I hear this, because it fits with what I can see and I suspect that the neighbour has decided to take matters into their own hands. Sadly, that's something I hear about far too often and many times the result is fatal. Occasionally, dogs do eat poisons accidentally and I have heard of vets having to treat animals after a dog has discovered their owner's chemicals or even drug stash, but it isn't common. Gareth insists that he and Paul never leave anything lying around that could harm Zenna.

The picture that he is building points more and more towards poisoning. I know that snail bait is often used when someone decides to harm an animal in this way. The baits are actually quite sweet, so the dog never realises that it's eating something that could make it seriously ill or even kill it.

I get Zenna's owner, Paul, on the phone. He's been visiting friends in Newcastle, just 150 kilometres away to the north. But I am sure right now he feels 1000 kilometres from where he wants to be. He confirms everything Gareth has told me and tells me to do whatever I have to do to help save Zenna. I make no promises.

There are two main ingredients that can be used in snail baits and, if I am right, either one of them could be causing these dire consequences. I decide to give Zenna the antidote to one of the poisons and if it doesn't work I'll try the other.

'I'm just going to give her an injection of Atropine,' I tell Gareth, who has been joined by some of Paul's work colleagues in the treatment room. With five police officers now in the clinic the law is certainly right behind Zenna. I never say it – but right now the main thing Zenna needs behind her is luck. I then administer a tablet to Zenna to make her bring up whatever is in her gut.

Gareth and his friends are all visibly distressed; it's obvious that they care very much for this dog. The atmosphere in the room is already tense so I make sure I don't add to it. I keep my voice steady and level and keep everyone informed about what I am doing. I have to keep focused and stay calm so Zenna stays calm.

The tablet does its job, and my worst suspicions are confirmed. Zenna regurgitates two massive snail baits. I really can't believe she managed to eat them – they're enormous. With this confirmation of my diagnosis I know that Zenna is in serious trouble. The toxins are already circulating in her system, and it will be a battle to keep her alive. To give her the best chance possible I know there's only one thing to do.

'We're going to have to move her to SASH,' I tell Gareth and his friends. Zenna needs intensive care and my clinic is not equipped for the high maintenance and intensive care she will need. While SASH – the Small Animal Specialist Hospital in Sydney's northwest – isn't exactly around the corner, the staff there are emergency specialists and they can give Zenna the around-the-clock care I know she's going to require.

Gareth and I carefully move Zenna's spasming body onto a towel and to the back seat of my car. It turns out Gareth just happens to be an intensive care nurse at a local children's hospital. I can think of no finer ally for Zenna if she is going to have any chance of beating the odds. And I couldn't have asked for a better person to accompany me. Gareth monitors Zenna's condition all the way, which means I can concentrate on getting us to SASH as quickly as possible. I only hope as I drive through Sydney's night-time traffic that I won't be too late. Zenna is holding on . . . but only just.

2

When Harry Met Chrissie

You probably think that because I am based in Bondi I mostly look after regular domestic pets, but this popular part of Sydney is well known for its colourful and varied residents – long-time locals, travellers looking to soak up the sun, young students seeking a beach lifestyle, artists, actors, musicians, families – and the animals in the area are just as eclectic.

Yes, a lot of my clinic time is spent dealing with the typical urban vet concerns – vaccinations, dogs having their nails clipped, puppies needing house-training, cats being wormed or de-sexed – but I also seem to come across everything from wondrous births to wildlife rescues, house calls to hair-raising emergencies like Zenna. To be honest, even before we started filming a television series in the clinic there was never a dull moment – and I wouldn't have it any other way.

I have wanted to be a vet ever since I can remember. My father is a vet in Newcastle, a city in New South Wales about two hours north of Sydney. Having him as a role model and being aware of what he did every day obviously had a strong impact on me. I learned a lot being around him and his clinic. Being a vet isn't the sort of job that can be kept separate from family life. We were all involved when Dad brought injured wildlife home to nurse back to health. At various times our backyard was home to chickens, ducks, koalas, kangaroos, horses, cows and a donkey as well as the more usual dogs, cats and birds. My family also had a farm about an hour's drive away from where we lived, and it was there I learned about the continuing demands of larger animals and further realised the obligations and the rewards that come with being a vet. The defining moment, though, was when my dog, Claude, became very ill. I was seventeen at the time and it really shook me up. I wanted to learn everything about the heart condition that eventually killed him. You can see my childhood was the perfect preparation for what I do now.

Though farm animals are rare in Bondi, birds are definitely not. Chrissie isn't one of my regulars and when she called to speak to me I picked up on not only the concern but the curiosity in her voice. Her beloved parrot, Harry, had apparently been losing his feathers for a couple of years, but only in particular places: on his chest and near the back of his neck. Chrissie was calling because it seemed to be getting worse and she was completely at a loss as to what to do. She didn't believe there was an immediate medical reason for Harry's condition – after all, she told me, he seemed so spirited and always received good food and had a caring environment. I decided to make a house call to see whether there was a clue in Harry's home. There are many things that can cause problems like this in birds: parasites and vitamin deficiencies are both possibilities.

In my mind, house calls are a necessary part of my job. At the clinic we have to fit within a certain timeframe – our consultations are scheduled to be completed in fifteen minutes. Of course we can't always stick to this. Emergencies or unexpected treatments are always dealt with, which can then throw the whole day's timetable out the window. And quite often owners have either left work to come to the clinic and have to get back, or they're rushing in before or after work or other commitments. During a home visit I have more time to spend and I have the opportunity to check out the environment in which an animal is living. This can often help me work out the cause of any health or behavioural issue more easily than within the unnatural and sometimes unnerving confines of the clinic. It is completely understandable that pets are a lot more relaxed when I see them at home. In fact, a recent study concluded that seventy-five per cent of animals show noticeable signs of stress and anxiety when they're coming to a vet clinic. Not unlike white-coat anxiety in people or the dread of the dentist!

My visit to Harry's place would turn out to be time well spent and, eventually, give me all the answers I needed.

As soon as I meet Chrissie, and before I even sight Harry, I have a part of the puzzle. Chrissie is not only vibrantly dressed – in almost parrot-like colours – but her voice is dramatic and sounds, dare I say, a bit parrot-esque too. I have an inkling that this may be an important clue to helping me work out what's really wrong with Harry.

I ask Chrissie to show me where Harry lives in the house, and it appears he has the run of the living area: there is no cage, just a number of perches for him in various places. Next I check out Harry's diet, which turns out to be a gourmet spread of caraway seeds soaked in flaxseed oil, sprouted legumes, which Chrissie makes herself, and other assorted fancy foods. Clearly, Chrissie is dedicated to providing Harry with the best, but this food is all a bit extravagant. When I inform her that Harry really doesn't need such an elaborate diet, Chrissie looks disappointed. So far, all I can tell is that Harry is a much-loved, if overindulged, pet. Then I see him in action with Chrissie's husband, John. And wow, it's hard not to miss the signs that Harry really does not like John – and John doesn't exactly love Harry, either. Just for the short time I am there I can see Harry behaves aggressively around John, who reacts much as you'd expect: he gets cranky. As you would when you have a set of claws and a beak bearing down on you. And Harry gets cranky back, squawking and flapping his wings, and also performing what I can only describe as the most dominant aggressive gesture possible: he simulates having sex with John's arm. Harry is trying to tell John to get lost. And the reason? Well, strange as it sounds, Harry is head over feet in parrot love with Chrissie.

It's not unusual for parrots to become besotted with their owners. Parrots are great thinkers and Harry, with a lifestyle that gives him too much time to use his mind, has become caught up in the world of the humans he lives with. Plus you can't help but feel there's a little human that exists in his head. He doesn't have to defend himself against predators (unless you count John) or find food, so this highly intelligent animal has spent his time over-interpreting Chrissie's care and affection for him and obsessing over those signals a little bit too much. Chrissie may be guilty of encouraging this obsessive behaviour because, like most people, she loves the fact that Harry is besotted with her. Owners do take pleasure in this kind of extreme attention from their pets. After all, they believe they're seeing the animal's true personality and affection. And it's all directed at them. So it allows them to feel even more attached!

Harry's obsession with Chrissie still doesn't tell me how and why he's been losing his feathers for so long. But I have an idea and, most importantly, a plan to see if I am right. Chrissie and John have a video camera, so we set it up on a tripod aimed at Harry's perch in the kitchen and then I ask them to do something that is guaranteed to provoke Harry and, if it works, provide the definitive answer to his falling feathers.

Chrissie and John embrace in front of their parrot and then leave the house, closing the door firmly behind them. After waiting outside for a few minutes, unseen by Harry, we then go back in. There is a small pile of feathers underneath Harry's perch that wasn't there when we left. What we see on the recorder is quite extraordinary. As soon as we left, Harry started plucking out his own feathers with his beak. One by one, he yanked them out of the skin on his chest and his upper back. Pushing through the pain – almost as though he was punishing himself. As I suspected, there is a simple explanation for his condition: Harry is a self-mutilator.

Chrissie and John are amazed that Harry would do this to himself. I am not. It's clear that Harry is a highly anxious bird. I see many nervous pets these days – often because their owners spend less time with them and yet demand more of them. Pets are no longer creatures that belong in the backyard – we want them to be part of the family, to have a name we call out like any other household member, yet nothing else we do with them implies that level of commitment or attachment. If you think about it, most of us don't really spend that much time with our pets, but when we do, as if to compensate, we spoil them.

Harry gets a lot of attention from Chrissie, but he still has a lot of time on his own to think and grow anxious. And the fact he plucks out his own feathers is a manifestation of his stress, just like a human chewing their fingernails. If you're nervous you need an outlet – it's a way of expressing the angst and frustration. As I mentioned before, if a bird isn't in its natural environment then it's not spending all its time finding food and flying around with its friends. It therefore has nothing else to distract it from a nagging concern or frustration. So in the end, there's nothing else to do apart from pick at their own feathers. And the strange thing is that Harry probably *enjoys* pulling out his feathers; that's the darker side of this behaviour. When the bird feels the pain it's letting out its anxiety. This also releases serotonin, the feel-good hormone; a natural kick which it can become addicted to.

Harry definitely needs some treatment for his advanced case of anxiety. My solution – to Chrissie's surprise – is to put him on Prozac, which is usually prescribed for humans with depression. I don't prescribe this medication often, but Harry really does need something to help him become less anxious. The Prozac should make him feel calmer, but a few things at home will also have to change, otherwise the behaviour may return. Chrissie needs to be less indulgent of Harry because, basically, inside every parrot is a potential stalker who just feeds on any little bit of interest it receives. Chrissie has to take a step back when he squawks; she can't be in such close contact with him as this reinforces his negative behaviours. So kisses, close chats and those secretive little dinners for two will have to stop. Harry was willing to mutilate himself in an attempt to deal with what he felt was unrequited love, so Chrissie has to start treating him like a bird, not a loving fan, as a way of breaking the news to him.

All going well, I am sure John will be pleased not to have an obsessed rival competing for Chrissie's affections!

What are the signs that my animal is becoming anxious?

Anxiety in animals is more common than you would suspect and there are a few signs you can watch out for:

- Does your animal tremble or shake?
- Does your animal hide or try to move away when someone they don't know well enters a room?
- Do you find they urinate (or worse) in inappropriate places?
- Are they listless and sleep a great deal?
- Are they hyper-alert and overstimulated?
- Do they pant heavily or breathe rapidly?
- Are they very demanding of your attention and want to be with you constantly?
- Do they bark, whine or whimper most of the time?
- Do they freak out when confined?

Your local vet can help you with strategies to deal with an anxious pet. They can also make sure there is no underlying medical condition contributing to unusual or disruptive behaviour.

3

Saving
Zenna

After one of those horrific car trips that seem much longer than they actually are, Gareth and I carry a very limp, extremely sick Zenna into SASH. Even though Zenna has expelled the snail baits it looks like her intestine could still be hiding some – plus their toxins are still working through her system. At this point she is closer to death than life. I am relieved that we made it here with Zenna still fighting.

Dr Lisa Chimes, the vet on night duty at SASH, meets us as we walk in. I know Zenna will be in good hands.

Not surprisingly, Lisa has always loved animals; I think this is the most important characteristic a vet can have. And Lisa's story is a familiar one: 'When I was a young kid, I was always rescuing birds and finding lost dogs on the side of the road,' she has explained. With a background like that, becoming a vet might have seemed a logical choice for her, but it wasn't something she considered until quite late in her schooling. Her father, a dentist, had once said to her, 'You'll never be able to be a vet; you won't be able to put animals down, you're not strong enough, you'll never be able to do it,' and she agreed with him. So despite the fact she spent a lot of her high school years rescuing animals and doing charity work for animal societies, it wasn't until she reached her final year that she realised she *could* be a vet and set her sights on that goal. Just before starting work at SASH Lisa completed an internship in emergency veterinary medicine in Melbourne, so I knew she was the perfect person to be looking after this very sick dog.

Lisa helped take Zenna to a treatment room and began to prepare her for a gastric lavage. It doesn't matter if it is an animal or a human, the way to deal with poisoning or overdose is to pump out the stomach, clearing out its contents. This is a procedure that involves feeding a tube into the gut via either the mouth or the nose, pouring warm water down the tube to fill up the stomach and then emptying it out, thereby helping to eliminate any toxins. This is the very last step that can be taken for Zenna, who will then be closely monitored overnight by Lisa and the other staff at SASH – but there's still no guarantee she'll survive. Zenna ate so much of the extremely toxic snail bait that it makes her situation very tough.

The next few hours will decide her future. If she can metabolise the toxin that's left in her system after the lavage, keep her temperature down and begin to show some significant signs of improvement, then there is hope. But we have done all we can – her survival now depends entirely on her.

4

A Penguin
Called Paddy

Most people living in urban Australia are used to seeing wildlife – even in the inner city you can still find lots of possums, and no matter where you are the chances of seeing cockatoos, kookaburras, rainbow lorikeets, king parrots and perhaps the odd galah are pretty good. But there's a whole lot more wildlife out there in the suburbs than you realise.

In Melbourne, for example, it's not uncommon to find snakes, because they're drawn to the water of the Yarra River. In Brisbane you will regularly find fruit bats in your garden and geckoes in your home. And around the waters of Sydney, where I live, you'll see the odd visiting whale, frolicking dolphins and you could quite possibly stumble upon a seal sunning itself on a rock. A vet in Australia may be called on at any time to look after local wildlife and though it is more common in rural areas to see kangaroos, wallabies, platypuses and echidnas, you'd be amazed at what seems to be attracted to the bright lights of Bondi!

While it might look tranquil, Sydney Harbour can be a frantic place. Yachts, speedboats, fishermen and fast-moving ferries all dart and weave their way out of the paths of the large tankers and cruise ships that send off huge waves as they shudder into port. But amazingly, among all these near-misses and noise, fairy penguins manage to find themselves a home. Because of the bustle it's not exactly the safe sanctuary it once would have been for the small bird. However, when I meet Paddy the penguin, it isn't a human-operated vessel that's causing him damage; something far smaller but even more dangerous is taking its toll.

Paddy had ventured away from the harbour and was found looking a bit worse for wear close to the rocks at nearby Clovelly Beach – south of Bondi. The person who found him placed a call to WIRES. The New South Wales Wildlife Information and Rescue Service is an organisation that aims to protect and care for injured wildlife. They have some facilities of their own, but rely on local vet clinics – including mine – to provide shelter and medical attention for wild animals. If, for example, you find an injured cockatoo or possum in your back garden, WIRES are the people to call for advice and to find a carer.

Barry, a volunteer from WIRES, calls me and we arrange to meet at the beach to check out if this report of a penguin is for real. To both my and the local dog population's surprise (who are circling worryingly close) the report of a penguin is very real. This isn't the first penguin I've come across – as a kid I cared for a penguin called Petie for six months. So it seems logical that the trend should continue. I decide to call this new penguin Paddy.

After examining the bird it is clear that he is very weak. Penguins normally have a good covering of fat, but as I feel around his sternum (breast bone) I can immediately feel it is not as plump as it should be. Quite aside from the stress that Barry and I are no doubt causing just by being close and handling him, his system is noticeably under strain. I know that when a fairy penguin is going through the process of moulting it uses up a lot of energy, and if that particular bird hasn't put enough energy into its bank via its fat reserves, it can't draw enough out during these periods to sustain itself and keep it healthy. And if this is Paddy's problem and he's come ashore to rest, there isn't the necessary food available on the rocks at Clovelly that could help re-energise him. It is a vicious cycle: he won't be able to feed and so his condition will deteriorate further. All of this spells major trouble for this bird.

I let Barry know my initial diagnosis is malnourishment – a very dangerous state for an animal who needs to have a large layer of fat to keep him warm in the depths of the ocean. It is obvious I'll need to take Paddy back to the clinic to do some further tests, because even in a harbour as busy as Sydney there should be enough food for him to eat, so I need to find out the underlying cause of his condition.

*   *   *

The most basic tests I can do are to weigh and measure Paddy. I also check him for external parasites and take a faecal sample to look for internal parasites. After studying this sample under the microscope I can see the most likely cause of Paddy's sorry state. He *is* harbouring a parasite – put simply, Paddy has worms! This means that whatever Paddy eats is not being absorbed into his own body, because the worms are robbing him of vital nutrients.

Paddy is not going to be cured immediately. After administering a worming drug to get rid of the parasites, he will need some close attention and careful feeding to build his system back up so he can survive in his natural environment. With the beeps and drips, phones ringing and dogs barking I know the clinic is not the best place for this process. Someone needs to take Paddy home.

I make a call.

I don't see wildlife cases every day of the week at the clinic, but they certainly make my life more interesting when they do turn up. Every qualified vet in this country is trained to look after wildlife and we all do this free of charge. A few years ago a study looked at how much Australian vets donate in terms of time and money to caring for wildlife and it's in the tens of millions of dollars per year. After all, you can't really bill nature for a course of antibiotics can you? This is our special opportunity and obligation as Australian vets, and it's part of the challenge of this job that I love so much. I like the fact that out of the blue I might have to treat a fairy penguin or a blue-tongue lizard and these cases help me maintain and build on my skills. But the truth is, these animals are the Aussie battlers that have been pushed out of their normal habitats by humans and their introduced pets, so it's important to look after them. As if to apologise for the inconvenience caused! If I can do my bit to keep these creatures alive and healthy in the city, then I'm more than happy to do it.

Autumn and spring are the busiest times for wild patients in my clinic. Most native animals breed in spring and the young typically start to make their own way in the world around autumn. The young are open to attack from wild and domestic predators and a mating animal can be even more territorial than usual. With the increased pressures, many of the animals can be pushed out of their local area and often into the path of cars. At those peak seasons I see three to five wildlife cases a week.

About a third of such instances I see in Bondi are possums. Another third would be birds and the rest fit into the 'what are you doing in Bondi?' category! Anything from kangaroos to geckoes to snakes. Really, any animal people may find either in the street, their own garden or on the beach – like Paddy.

My flatmate is getting used to calls from me asking if he'd mind an extra houseguest, so when his phone rings and I'm on the end of the line suggesting I have a sushi-eating, beach-loving bird – I reckon I might be able to talk him around!

After growing up in a household where I never knew what animal Dad might bring home to look after, I don't find it strange to live around the needs of an animal. But to most people it is a big ask and I'm lucky that flatmates like Brad are so laid-back.

The fact is, it's not easy to hand-feed a penguin who's too weak to feed himself. Paddy's traumatised by captivity and at a stage where he doesn't actually realise that he has to eat, so I have to make the decision for him. Even so, I don't want to force fish down the little bird's throat – nor do I want to lose my fingers in the process – but it's proving very hard to get him to eat. The eventual solution is to use a pair of chopsticks to place pilchards deep in Paddy's throat, so all he has to do is swallow. After 'borrowing' some chopsticks from the sushi restaurant down the road (not that they will want them back – the smell of pilchards doesn't go away easily!) Brad pitches in to help and between us we manage to get some fish into Paddy. Then I put him in a cage and cover it with a towel to help him sleep. I place him in our shower cubicle and resist the urge to turn on the tap, telling myself it won't quite give him the impression that he's still out to sea that he might be looking for!

The next morning Paddy is still alive. You never know what the stress of captivity will do to a weakened animal so there is always a risk that even though you are trying to help, the very fact it is cooped up in a strange place can kill it. Thanks to a number of trips over to the beach with a bucket I fill a paddling pool with seawater so he can have a splash around. When I hold him, I am very pleased to note how powerful his flippers are – in fact, when he pushes them against me it's like he's trying to slap me. Some thanks that is!

When I put him in the pool I watch closely to see how he performs. He immediately seems more at home. His eyes brighten, he wiggles his small flippers, has a bit of a shake and a preen. It seems to me he is getting stronger but he still has a long road to recovery. I know that I'm at the limit of what I can do for him and I certainly can't keep him in my back garden indefinitely . . . After all, even with his personal paddling pool it's no Pacific Ocean!

Once I know he isn't rapidly deteriorating and the worms are taken care of there is hope for Paddy's rehabilitation. I start to make plans. It's time to call Taronga Zoo. Taronga is a world-renowned zoo on the foreshores of Sydney Harbour. The zoo often takes wildlife that need a bit of extra care. While some patients never leave the zoo because they're not able to fend for themselves, the zoo does hope to get them to the point where they can be returned to their natural habitat. It is exactly what I would like to see for Paddy, and the people at Taronga Zoo are better placed than me to make that happen.

Of all the wildlife cases I see at the clinic, there's only one type of animal I can't treat: bats. It may seem harsh, but as far as bats go there is always the possibility that they may be carrying the lyssavirus, which is a rare rabies-like infection that can be fatal in humans. So far only two cases of lyssavirus have been identified in Australia, but it can take years for the symptoms to present themselves and once the infection is established there is nothing that can be done. There is a preventative vaccine available, but it's often just not worth the risk.

So I don't see any bats. But I do see plenty of possums. It seems to me people either love possums or hate them. And that feeling hinges strongly on whether you have possums in your roof or not. I'll go out on a limb and say that I like possums, and I think that if there weren't so many of them in our suburbs keeping many of us awake at night then we'd probably all love them. Let's face it, they are mostly cute and I can confidently state that I have met the full spectrum of possum personalities: some are very calm, polite and well mannered, and others are insistent on trying to take off your finger – which actually happened to me once (well, nearly). I still have the finger, but the possum had a good go at detaching it!

The two most dangerous wild animals I've ever treated are snakes and eagles. In times of drought both of these animals will move in towards the cities to feed, because their natural food sources – rodents and other small animals – are diminished. They have to roam wider and expose themselves to humans more often to get enough food to survive. Recently, as large parts of Australia have been in drought, I have had the opportunity to interact with these risky creatures more often.

We all know about the dangers of snakes, but with eagles and falcons I have to tell you it's their massive claws you have to watch out for. They can rip open human skin as easily as they can their usual prey. They don't discriminate. On separate occasions I have treated a sea eagle and a small wedgetail eagle and both had claws that were half the size of my finger. If I'd handled either of them the wrong way and they'd grabbed hold of my hand, their claws would have gone through my skin to the bone. Fortunately, the eagles didn't get as close as the finger-loving possum or else I would definitely be minus a digit.

Two weeks after I drop Paddy at Taronga Zoo I get to see him one last time. The zoo staff have done a wonderful job and he now has a healthy-looking coat, a new penguin mate, and is definitely much tubbier. It is time for him to be released back into the wild as he is ready to fend for himself and deal with the cold ocean depths. I'm almost sorry to see him go, but I feel proud that I had a small part in keeping him alive and giving him another chance. And, who knows, if he sticks to Sydney Harbour, maybe I'll spot him again one day . . . though hopefully not as a patient.

What Should You Do if You Find an Injured Animal?

Injured wildlife

1. Check first to see if the animal is actually injured – there is no need to approach it unless completely necessary.
2. Use common sense: if the animal looks dangerous, stay well away from it.
3. Try not to make too much noise around the animal.
4. If you have to pick up the animal, be as gentle as possible.
5. Ensure any children or other animals (such as pets) are kept away from the injured animal.
6. Do not give the animal any food, especially cow's milk.
7. If the animal is deceased, move it away from the road.
8. If the dead animal is a kangaroo, wallaby or possum, check its pouch for joeys.
9. Contact a wildlife rescue organisation (numbers listed below).

Other types of animals

Follow steps 1 to 7 above, then use the *Yellow Pages* to find the veterinary clinic or animal hospital nearest to you. If you can, take the animal there.

Wildlife Rescue Organisations Around Australia

Australian Capital Territory

WIRES

13000 WIRES or 1300 094 737

New South Wales

Sydney Wildlife

(02) 9413 4300 (24-hour service)

www.sydneywildlife.org.au

WIRES

13000 WIRES or 1300 094 737

www.wires.org.au

Northern Territory

Wildcare Inc Alice Springs

0419 221 128 (24-hour service)

Wildlife Rescue Darwin

0409 090 840 (24-hour service)

South Australia

Fauna Rescue of South Australia

08 8289 0896

www.faunarescue.org.au

Tasmania

Parks and Wildlife Service Tasmania

03 6233 6556 (24-hour service)

www.parks.tas.gov.au/index

Queensland

Far North Queensland Wildlife Rescue

07 4053 4467 (24-hour service)

www.fnqwildliferescue.org.au

Wildcare Australia

07 5527 2444

www.wildcare.org.au

Victoria

Wildlife Victoria

1300 0WILDLIFE or 1300 094 535 (24-hour service)

www.wildlifevictoria.org.au

Western Australia

Broome Wildlife Care and Rescue

0408 860 022 (24-hour service)

www.broomewildlifecare.com

5

A Happy Ending

When Zenna's owner, Paul, arrives at SASH he is beside himself to see his beloved dog lying, almost lifeless, with tubes and drips attached to her. His mate, Gareth, is still there to support him, but there's really no comfort in a situation like this.

Paul is completely devastated at what has happened: 'To try to kill a dog, which they would have done if Gareth hadn't arrived in time . . . It's got to be the lowest of lows.'

I have to agree with him.

I have seen several cases of malicious dog poisoning – the tell-tale sign being animals swallowing snail bait despite the fact their owners didn't have any in their house or yard. Even when the owners suspect someone of poisoning, it is very rare for charges to be laid, because it's just so hard to prove who was responsible. I don't like adding Zenna to the list of patients I have seen as a consequence of such behaviour.

But could Paul being a police officer have played a part? His uniforms were often hanging on the line, apparently. But even with the law at his disposal this isn't Paul's focus at the moment. His only concern is for his dog.

It turns into a long, hard night for Zenna. Paul is eventually persuaded to go home and rest and Dr Lisa Chimes and the team at SASH keep a close eye on her. Gradually her body temperature decreases and as it falls the risk of brain damage diminishes. Zenna is putting up a huge fight against the poison and her organs seem to be meeting the challenge, metabolising the toxin and eliminating it from her system. By morning she is looking a lot better and her vital signs are strong. Both Lisa and I believe this was in large part due to her youth – an older dog probably wouldn't have made it.

When a weary Paul arrives back at SASH, he is thrilled to see the obvious turnaround.

'To see her lying there last night broke my heart. But to see her again today . . . alive; I'm ecstatic, relieved.'

Once Lisa is happy with Zenna's condition she gives the okay for her to leave. Paul is eager to get his pet home, but I'm not surprised when he tells me he's decided to move to ensure that this will never happen to Zenna again. I'm very pleased this case is going to have a happy ending . . . and I hope it's the last time I have to treat an animal that is put in a life-threatening situation by spiteful, selfish and ruthless human behaviour. Sadly, I don't think it will be.

6

A Deadly Visitor

If you are a long-term dog or cat owner I am sure you are aware of the potentially lethal danger a tick presents to your animals. This is one type of wildlife our pets could definitely do without! These tiny parasites – from one millimetre to one centimetre in size – are one of the most common problems a vet sees in the summer months, in dogs especially, all along the East Coast of Australia and especially in the bushland pockets around Sydney. Even in Bondi they are a problem occasionally and in the clinic I am regularly confronted by the life-threatening reality that tick-poisoning presents.

Ticks usually attach themselves to dogs or cats when the animal is playing in grass and around bushy areas. Dogs are inquisitive creatures who like to get their snouts into everything – and unfortunately curiosity can take its toll on any animal when they pick up a tick. One recent case I know of is that of Polar, an eleven-month-old Samoyed. Polar didn't come into my clinic – he was taken directly to SASH when his back legs suddenly become paralysed.

Samoyeds are very furry dogs – they are meant to live in cold countries like Russia. In a country like Australia with a bushy, humid environment, all that fur acts as an invitation to hungry ticks looking for a place to stay – they'll jump right on and burrow in on such an animal. The abundant fur of the Samoyed also makes these insidious creatures very hard to find, even to the most experienced eye.

When Polar is brought into SASH by one of his young owners, Lucas, he is in a very bad way. Lisa is the vet on duty and after a quick chat to Lucas about Polar's recent activity and home environment, as well as observation of the paralysis in Polar's back legs, she concludes right away that the dog is probably harbouring a tick. As Polar has already had one tick bite in the past few months, Lucas recognised the signs and knew to get him some help quickly. Even with this speedy response, Polar has already been paralysed for three or four hours by the time he arrives at SASH. And that can be long enough to kill a fit and healthy animal.

Lisa knows how serious the situation is and that she has to find the tick and remove it before it injects any more toxin into Polar. A tick's toxin is pumped into the bloodstream and binds at the ends where the muscles meet the nerves, paralysing the animal that is acting as its unwitting host. The paralysis starts at the back legs and moves up the body towards the lungs, which means that eventually an animal's respiration system is impacted and it can stop breathing and die. Other bodily systems are also affected by tick toxin and so death can be drawn out and painful for any afflicted animal. There is an antiserum for the toxin, but for it to have a chance to work on an animal it's best if the tick can be found before it does too much damage.

Sometimes finding the tick is a tough job. Even engorged with blood they can be small and on an animal like Polar with so much thick fur it is the proverbial needle-in-a-haystack situation. Lisa gets to work with clippers, shaving off Polar's long white coat and simultaneously searching for a tick. She finds what looks like a tick bite on Polar's neck – but no tick. So she keeps searching. It's a long process, and all the while Polar is getting progressively worse, to the point where he can't swallow. One of the vet nurses takes over the clipping to give Polar a closer shave – 'Never get a vet to clip,' says Lisa with wry humour – but there's still no sign of the tick. Lisa can't hold off any longer and an antiserum is administered.

Three or four hours after Polar's arrival, he has a new haircut and a dose of antitoxin but at this point the substance is still progressing through Polar's system and his front legs are now paralysed. The antiserum can take up to twenty-four hours to start working, so in the meantime Polar's symptoms need to be managed to give the best possible chance of survival. As usual, Lisa is one step ahead.

'I can't imagine how hard it would be to feel like this,' says Lisa as she gives Polar some oxygen to make his breathing easier. Lisa needs to keep Polar in overnight to monitor his progress, and to be sure the tick is not still pumping poison, the search for it will continue.

The next morning Polar is alert although 'not completely out of the danger zone,' says Lisa. 'His swallow reflex is not perfect after the tick bite. There is always the risk that he might inhale some of his food, so we have to just feed him very slowly.'

Despite this, it seems Polar has made a really quick recovery. As Lisa states, 'I usually find it takes about twenty-four hours for us to notice some improvement and in this situation it's been less than twelve and he's already made a dramatic change.'

Polar's family call to find out how he is doing and are told the good news. Lucas's older brother, Quentin, comes to pick up Polar to take him home, but before he can go Lisa wants Polar to prove that his legs are steady – and despite the slippery floor at the hospital he manages to show her he is regaining his ability to move. Quentin is delighted to see his family pet, but visibly surprised to see Polar's new look. 'His coat is completely gone. He went from looking like a polar bear to almost a lion. But it's just good seeing him alive, happy, strong,' he says with a smile.

The outcome for most dogs with tick bites is usually good if the dog is taken to the vet in time and can be monitored overnight, but prevention is still the best form of defence.

Accordingly, Lisa's advice to Quentin is to keep Polar shaved – although this is clearly not how Samoyeds are supposed to look. As Lisa says, 'When dogs have really long hair and the owners know they live in a tick area, they probably should clip their dogs over the summer months, just so they can check them easily.'

Lisa's absolutely right: the best way to prevent ticks poisoning your animal is to thoroughly check them over every day, because if you get the parasites off your pet before they've had time to inject their toxin, then you can hopefully prevent a visit to the vet at best, and the death of your beloved pet at worst.

Some dogs do need to have their fur kept long, particularly if they are show dogs. 'But,' says Lisa, 'it's just going to make the job a lot harder. You should brush the dog thoroughly, check it, part the hair – but you're just not going to be able to check them as well as you would if they had short hair.'

To check your dog or cat for ticks, look in their ears, in all the orifices, under the limbs – in any really warm and moist spots, because that's usually where ticks go. As dogs often poke through things with their heads, you should check the head and shoulder area, as well as their bottoms and private parts, and under their feet. There are also medications that you can put on them that can kill the ticks but, as Lisa says, 'they're not 100 per cent guaranteed, so you still have to check your animal'.

It's important, too, to keep your pet's environment in mind when assessing the risk of a tick bite. Lisa explains:

'In the wild a lot of the ticks come from the native animals and the [domestic] animal needs to be in fairly close contact with the bush or the other animal for the tick to jump from one to the other. Usually, they pick up ticks when they're rummaging through bush areas, but if you get new plants in, or new grass or turf, you don't know where those plants have come from: they could be carrying ticks. When dogs exhibit signs of a tick bite in areas that don't usually have ticks and someone's recently gardened, people have to consider that the ticks could have come in the gardening package. For people in country areas and the lower New South Wales coast the problems are year round.'

So it's important to be vigilant with your animal – keep checking them for ticks and if you find that a normally healthy dog or cat suddenly can't use one or more of its legs, take them to the vet straightaway. Talk to your vet about preventative measures, be aware of changes to your pet and act fast if you are suspicious that your animal may be affected by a tick.

7

A Very
Serious Incident

Just like in a hospital dealing with humans, if an animal comes into my clinic in a crisis situation, you just can't wait around. Emergencies are always seen immediately. And there is perhaps nothing worse than seeing an animal that has been hit by a car . . . except perhaps when I find out that the person who hit the animal took off without stopping. And this is just the situation I face when Dawn Hardy and her daughter Fiona come across a young dog that has been hit by a car and rush it to me. 'Someone ran over its whole head and then just kept driving,' Fiona tells me. 'Just left it there.'

Though I won't ever understand how someone could run over an animal and not even stop – to me it's beyond callous – sadly, it doesn't surprise me. It's a lot more common than I would like. For now, I convince myself that maybe the driver didn't know – just so I can concentrate on the task at hand.

When an animal comes in with injuries from a car, we try to do everything we can to ensure that it survives. In this case the dog is not in a good way at all. I have to assess the animal quickly and my first priority is to ensure that there's no bleeding. I check it for external wounds and also for any signs of internal bleeding. Some of her injuries are obvious: she has tyre marks on her face and one eye is bulging. That alone tells me there is a good chance her brain is swelling from the concussion she's no doubt sustained, so I decide to give her some cortisone to help with that. With this amount of trauma to her skull, it's amazing that this dog is still alive.

Sara Ashdown, one of the clinic nurses, is working with me and we administer morphine to help control the dog's pain. At least we can make her comfortable while we continue to work out the full extent of her injuries. And I have to ask this animal to trust us, to try to understand that we're doing the best we can for her. I'm concerned about some rigidity in her back legs, but there could be a number of causes behind this; shock, spinal trauma or serious pain among them. I'll have to wait to investigate further, but right now stabilising this badly injured dog is more important.

While Sara and I are focusing on the immediate problems, nurse Neil Coy has the task of trying to find this dog's owner. He scans the injured animal for a microchip. Microchipping has made a vet's life much less complicated. This new technology makes Neil's job much easier. Because this dog is microchipped we learn that the dog's name is Jackie and we're able to contact her owner quickly. And in a trauma case like this, time is very important. It's not hard to understand why these are the type of phone calls I dread making. Informing someone that their animal is critically injured takes an emotional toll but it is obviously nothing on what the owner, Steve, has to go through. Not surprisingly, it doesn't take long for Steve to arrive at the clinic. But Jackie can't see him. Because of the trauma to her skull, she's blind. As soon as Steve approaches her and she can sense him, smell him, her response is immediate. She uses every last bit of energy to try to get up and be close to him. Because of her other injuries she can't wag her tail but we can all see how happy she is that he is there. It is very touching.

Steve is very upset. He tells me that Jackie is just fourteen months old and that she is his best buddy.

'I got her as a companion because I live by myself,' he says. 'I wanted a dog to have a bit of company.'

Jackie's youth and her special role in Steve's life only make what's happened to her more horrific. It is obvious to me that Steve would be devastated if he lost her. I am determined to do my utmost to make sure that doesn't happen.

The sombre mood that settled on everyone at the clinic when we first saw the badly injured Jackie doesn't improve when we find out the reason for Jackie's accident. At the time a friend of Steve's had been looking after her. The friend had taken Jackie for a walk to the local shops and left her tied up to a signpost on the footpath while he went into a store. Security camera footage from a local shop showed someone, for some unknown and inexplicable reason, untying Jackie's leash from the post, unclipping the leash from the dog and then taking off – with the leash. Of all the stupid things to do, this has to be the top of any list – why would anyone steal a leash and leave a little dog to fend for herself on the side of a busy road? It's no wonder Jackie ran out into the path of a car – she must have been very confused in this unfamiliar location. I can't believe the senselessness of what has happened and the turn of events that has led to Jackie being so badly injured. It seems the fates have conspired against this little dog and she is in for a mighty battle.

I continue to monitor Jackie throughout the night. The next morning, if she's stable, I will X-ray her to make sure there's nothing I've missed. Because Jackie's injuries were so serious and life-threatening when she was brought in, checking for fractures is low on the immediate to-do list – fractured legs are painful and need treatment, but they will heal. In a case like Jackie's it is necessary to deal with the most urgent injuries first and get her stabilised before any other treatment is given. I wish I could tell Steve a broken leg was her only problem.

8

Elroy's Pride

I've lived in Bondi for a few years now. It's my home, and I love it. Let's face it – for a guy who likes to surf, what's not to love about having the ocean at your front door and your work in the same suburb? There's also the restaurants, the cosmopolitan lifestyle and the colourful people. But I'm sure that residents of other parts of Sydney and, indeed, other parts of Australia have an impression of Sydney's most famous beach that is perpetuated by the photos and footage they see of glamorous people swanning around in swimming costumes and very little else. Did you see Paris Hilton being mobbed on the sands of Bondi? I guess what I'm trying to say is that some people may think that Bondi residents could be a little – how shall I say this? – concerned with their appearance. And the truth is, like anywhere, some are. But I'm fairly sure they've never thought of Bondi's dogs the same way. And neither had I. Until I met Elroy.

Elroy is a strapping ten-month-old bulldog owned by Bree and her boyfriend. They have brought Elroy to see me about a behavioural problem. There's nothing really wrong with him – in fact, it's more the case that everything is too right. Elroy's body is doing what it's meant to do when he hits his stride as an adult dog: it's producing a lot of testosterone. And that's making him a little too aggressive. Elroy's testosterone-laden behaviour is partly because of his breed – bulldogs are not exactly shy, retiring types – but also his own personality. In a pack of dogs Elroy might well be the alpha male, but here at Bondi Beach, on the end of a leash held by Bree, Elroy is just a bundle of hormones with nowhere to use them. So he expresses his masculinity by barrelling into unsuspecting strangers, forward-charging stairs and generally making it hard for Bree to control him. Bree thinks Elroy is a lovely dog, but it's hard for others to tell when all he does is grunt and try to mate with everything he sees. His owner can barely handle him when they're out walking: Elroy is becoming so strong that it's almost like *he's* walking *her*. But, funnily enough, those dog-loving Bondi residents are partly to blame. You see, when the extroverted Elroy lunges at a passer-by their natural reaction is to reach out and pat what appears to be a really friendly dog. The problem is that all the attention simply fuels Elroy's belief that this boisterous behaviour is what people want from him!

As Bree says, 'My expectations when I bought Elroy were that he would be a quiet bundle of joy that would just kind of laze about. Unfortunately, Elroy is the most energetic dog I've ever had. I don't normally let him off the lead, because he'll just run off and jump on people and eat people's food. I'm hoping that you can help. I'll do anything.'

The standard treatment for this kind of behaviour is to give the dog what is commonly known as 'the snip' – castration. It's certainly the most effective solution, as it completely arrests the production of testosterone. The dog could be put through behavioural training but that's akin to giving an eighteen-year-old boy instructions on life while there's heavy metal music playing in the room. In Elroy's case the heavy metal music is testosterone, drowning out any other signal he could possibly receive, so behavioural training would be a waste of time.

Bree is all in favour of neutering her dog. The catch? Her boyfriend is not. Sure, he sees the wisdom of the procedure – he doesn't dispute that something has to be done. But he is concerned that Elroy's appearance and perhaps 'presence' on the Bondi promenade will be so badly affected that he won't be able to hold up his doggy head in public. That's right: he thinks that Elroy will be embarrassed if he loses his crown jewels.

Now, I've seen dogs get embarrassed before. You've probably seen some dogs dressed up in weird outfits and they're clearly uncomfortable about it. I've also seen dogs with dodgy haircuts who don't look like they want to be out in public. Dogs do have some human-type sensitivities. But this is the first time that anyone has told me that they think their dog will be more traumatised by how he looks with his testes removed than by how he'll feel after the operation. Only in Bondi? Maybe. But I need to find a solution before Elroy pulls Bree's arm out of its socket. And I have an idea.

A year previously I visited Los Angeles in California — which is not unlike Sydney with its beach culture — and in Hollywood (of all places) I worked with a vet who specialised in something I thought I'd never see! Testicular implants for dogs, called Neuticles! I saw a lot of dogs who had the implants and the results were good both aesthetically and physically — there seemed to be no complications from the procedure. This may be the solution we need for Elroy.

I outline everything about the process, the risks and the benefits that are possible, as well as inform Bree of the cost. After discussing this further with her boyfriend, who wants to know the implants will be an appropriate size — namely, not too small — Bree decides to go ahead with castration and implantation. I am not sure what Elroy makes of the whole thing, but he will be a more manageable dog after the procedure and this is my chief concern.

After I place a call to Neuticles headquarters in the midwest of the United States I discover that there are four types of Neuticle, each available in quarter-inch increments. This is a country with the adage 'bigger is better' but I'm not sure if this applies to Neuticles as well. On further discussion with Gregg Miller, the inventor of Neuticles and founder of Neuticles Corporation, I discover that nature dictates the size — rather than the owner! Makes sense to me. After all, whatever you put in must be the same size as whatever you take out — otherwise how is it going to fit? I do some more research and then order what I think will be the right make and size and we book in Elroy for the operation.

When the day arrives, Bree is excited about Elroy's operation and the chances of bringing home a dog she can deal with. 'I feel like it will be so much relief at home and on our walks. I'm hoping it will make a difference.'

Inside the clinic, I talk through the operation with Bree so she is aware of what I am going to do. I ask her what her boyfriend thinks about it all.

'It wasn't hard convincing your boyfriend that silicone was the way to go?'

'Not at all,' says Bree. 'It just had to be done. I think every man likes silicone anyway . . . My boyfriend loves Elroy's personality, but he does realise that he's out of control, so it's definitely time to do something about it.'

I then show Bree the Neuticles I'm intending to sew into her bulldog.

'They're kind of . . .' She hesitates. I suspect I know why.

'Don't say small. Just don't say too small,' I say and smile hopefully.'

'They do look smaller than his, though,' Bree says, laughing.

'They're slightly compressed because they've been in air freight!' I explain.

I'm not sure that Bree accepts this rationale, but she'll just have to – it's time for her to say *arrivederci* to Elroy so we can get him into surgery. And, even then, he puts up a fight.

'He's even too crazy to say goodbye to!' Bree exclaims.

Before he goes on the table Elroy gets one last shot at being the alpha male: he gives us a hard time while we try to anaesthetise him. This compact bundle of muscle puts up a struggle as Nurse Mel tries to hold him down and I try to send him off to dreamland. (Later, we find out that the effort of holding Elroy actually caused ligament damage to Mel's shoulder. Now that's a strong dog!)

Even though this is a *slightly* comical operation, Elroy's behaviour highlights a very serious side to it: he is not only very tricky to *get* under anaesthetic, but he'll also be hard to *keep* under anaesthetic. We need him to be calm but at the same time I don't want to give him too much sedative to settle him down, as these drugs could have a dangerous effect on his already stressed-out body.

Once he is under I get started on the operation. Things are going well, until . . .

I'd estimated the size of Elroy's testes when I ordered the Neuticles, bearing in mind Paul's concerns, but for a moment it seems like I've given the little nugget too much credit: the Neuticles are in danger of not fitting inside Elroy's skin. This is a serious procedure and I don't take it lightly, but it is one of the more unusual operations in which I have ever been involved. To be blunt, for a moment there I feel like I am trying to slip a ping-pong ball into a slot meant for a marble. Normally when I perform this procedure on a dog I'm only taking something out; it's quite a challenge to then put something back in. Even though I'd observed this practice when I was in the US, performing it turns out to be a different matter altogether.

The whole time we monitor Elroy's vital signs and he sleeps on, unaware of the indignity he is experiencing. I don't even like to think what this alpha male would do if he was conscious of what was happening to him. It is impossible to know exactly what a dog's behaviour will be like after the operation, but I like to think that castration helps reveal a dog's true personality, once the thunder and lightning of rampaging hormones is removed. Hopefully it changes him from being the Bondi Casanova to the placid promenade dog Bree has always wanted.

Once it's all over, Elroy gets an overnight stay at the clinic. When Bree picks him up the next morning she is astonished at the difference. Granted, Elroy is still medicated so that is making him groggy and slow-moving, but she deserves to be hopeful that this may be a sign of things to come. And from all reports Elroy is now much easier to handle – he's the lovable creature Bree always thought he was. Plus he gets to keep his pride: he may no longer be an alpha male, but he still looks like one.

Elroy is the only dog I've ever operated on who has received testicular implants – and it's not often anyone can say they're the first to do something in Bondi, so Elroy should parade his new acquisitions with pride. I suspect he won't be the last such op I perform. I can only wonder at what is coming next: facelifts for Shar-Pei perhaps?

All joking aside, the serious aspect of Elroy's case was that his testosterone overload threatened to make him impossible for Bree to look after and live with. Although Elroy wasn't prone to biting, he is an extremely strong dog and when those hormones were surging through his body he was almost too strong and boisterous for Bree to manage. He could have slipped her grasp and been hit by a car, knocked over an elderly person or young child and injured them or even bitten someone eventually. It could have reached the point where Bree would have been unable to take him out in public, simply because his enthusiasm and energy made him unsafe as he charged at other people and dogs. And no walks outside would have almost certainly meant boredom and obesity issues for Elroy – not to mention a lack of enjoyable outside excursions for Bree!

Bree made the decision about Elroy's operation at the right time in his life, while he was still young. If she had waited much longer his behaviour would have become ingrained; instead of the operation being something that she would *like* to do, it would have become a necessity. Elroy was turning into a forceful, marauding creature who was a nightmare for Bree to handle. Now he's a much more manageable dog . . . with a secret.

Desexing Your Pet

- Seek advice from your vet as soon as you obtain a pet as to the most appropriate time for this procedure. This will vary depending on its breed, age and physical condition.

- A responsible pet owner has to consider the consequences of not desexing their animal. Finding a home for baby animals is not as easy as you would think.

9

A Heartbreaking Decision

The next morning I am very pleased that hit-and-run victim Jackie has made it through the night and seems out of immediate danger. I know she is still in a bad way but now she is stabilised it's time for her X-rays so I can determine the true extent of her injuries.

Our clinic, like most other vet surgeries, is equipped like a small hospital – we have everything we need to diagnose and treat all but the most extreme cases. I shudder to think what it would be like if I had to move a wounded dog to another part of the city for an X-ray – it would make things so much more distressing for the animal.

X-raying an animal isn't quite as easy as taking images of a human: you can't ask an animal to lie still and expect that it will heed the request. As a result, we have two options. Either sedate (or anaesthetise) them to keep them still or, if they are too sick to handle such a procedure, the nurses and I will have to hold their legs or head to ensure they don't move. We wear precautionary lead aprons to prevent the radiation affecting us – then we just cross our fingers that the machine has an accurate aim as we arrange and hold the animal in place.

I am sure some animals are extremely nervous about being on the X-ray table – it would seem strange, to be held down while something happens and you're not sure what. But Jackie is still so sick that she doesn't really notice. To be honest, I'm amazed she's made it this far. She's somehow survived the head trauma and the concussion; now she's doing her best to convince me that she can beat this whole thing. But I am incredibly worried about the lack of movement in her back legs. I am hoping that this is caused by spinal shock, which will wear off, but this is only the best-case scenario. Until I see the X-rays I won't know what she is up against. But since she has overcome every other hurdle I feel I'm entitled to feel hopeful.

Once we've taken the X-rays I sit with Jackie for a few moments. The thing I find most touching about her is that, because she can't see, she can only take comfort from being able to smell things. If I go near her she has a sniff of me and a little lick, as if to say, 'Are you helping me now?' I constantly wonder at animals' ability to soldier on. It seems that if they decide they do want to fight on, they have an amazing ability to push themselves just that little bit harder.

Once the films are ready I put them on the lightbox and scrutinise what they reveal about Jackie's wounded body. I don't have to look too closely or too long to find the bad news that I was desperately hoping not to see.

Jackie has a spinal fracture. And it's about as severe as they come. It's so serious that I know she will never walk again. After all she's been through it is emotionally devastating. This little dog had so much fight in her and means so much to her owner, Steve, that even though the odds were against her I had hoped there would be a positive outcome. But it is not to be. Jackie has an injury the equivalent of which in a human would render them a paraplegic. There is nothing I can do for Jackie and her quality of life would be negligible if she was kept alive.

The flash of anger I feel is overwhelming. When that idiot stole her lead he also stole her life. She just did what was natural and ran away. Now she's the victim of some person's stupidity and that person doesn't have to deal with the sight of this little dog in trouble. It's senseless and heartbreaking.

As Sara says, 'It never gets any easier. In fact, it sometimes gets harder, particularly as you get to know the animal and the people involved. We know with the animal that we would never let them suffer, but it's really hard for the people. That's what breaks your heart. It breaks my heart.'

My sense of frustration is beyond immense. These days it seems like there are so many things that *can* be fixed that it's even harder to take when there's something that *can't*. In a world where I am implanting silicone testicles in a dog, I struggle with the fact nothing can be done for Jackie. But it can't.

In any situation like this I work on an animal believing that there's a chance that they will make a recovery; and, more than the belief, there's hope too. I can't help but hope. I couldn't work as a vet – I couldn't even have thought about becoming a vet – if I didn't have some sense of empathy for the animals I'm treating. In every case like Jackie's I feel the animal's pain and misfortune and suffering, but I can't be a human being without feeling the owner's suffering as well. I have learned how much Steve loves his beloved pet and I know how devastated he will be.

I have to tell him the extent of Jackie's injuries and inform him that the only thing we can do for her is to put her to sleep. It is tough news to deliver and, as expected, Steve is distraught. He can't deal with the fact that the dog that means the world to him has been cruelly snatched from his life. The fact that she seemed a little better doesn't help him to come to terms with what has to be done. I give Steve as much time as he needs to say goodbye to his pet.

This part of my job is the most difficult and the circumstances that brought Jackie to this point make it even harder to take. But if I can't help Jackie recover to live a good life then my next priority is to ease her suffering and end her life as painlessly and as quickly as possible.

This day is not a good day.

10

Second
Best

Emergencies like Jackie's are a frequent occurrence in a suburban veterinary practice; in Bondi we'd see a case like hers at least once a week. If you think that humans have a hard time in an emergency, try to imagine what it would be like to be an animal: You're in pain, you're confused and panicked with no way of knowing where you are or what's happening to you. With no one speaking your language, you wouldn't know that what these strange people are doing to you is actually meant to help – not hurt.

I am always aware of the animal's emotional state when they come in, and it's usually the same as their owner's. It's taken a bit of practice for me to learn to stay calm, but it's an absolute necessity. In an emergency situation there's so much panic and so much confusion that even if I don't know what the problem is I'm obliged to keep my cool, because if I don't the pet will sense it and become even more stressed.

Pets are very good at picking up on body language and mood, and if they can sense that everyone in the room is panicking, they'll feel like they're well and truly entitled to join in. So it's as much for the pet as for the owner that I keep calm.

Lisa over at SASH has a different angle on managing stressful situations.

'I think one of the hardest parts of being a vet is dealing with the owners,' she says. 'Not in the sense that the owners are doing anything wrong or being aggressive or anything like that – it's because the owners are genuinely stressed about their animals, and when people are stressed they're irrational and they don't understand things as well as they normally would. And in that situation your emotions are just through the roof.

'People say that being a vet is like being a paediatrician because your patient can't talk and the doctor has to speak to the parents of the child to get the history, and the parents are stressed because they don't know what's wrong with their baby and the baby can't tell them what's wrong. So, likewise, dealing with the owners can be tough, but hopefully if your treatment is sensible and your approach to them is reasonable, then they'll come around. Those kinds of people skills are vital – it's important that we're not just becoming vets to treat the animals, because half of it is actually treating the owners as well. But the happy times outweigh all the stress – the animal comes in sick and the owners are crying and sad and then you fix them and they go home, and there's nothing better than that.'

For me, if I'm being honest, an emergency is the situation in which I feel as though I get the greatest emotional return for being a vet. I'm using every single skill I have – emotional and physical – and I'm also on a knife-edge trying to make sure I nail what's going on. It's the biggest test a vet can have, I think: those emergencies when time is of the essence, there's panic in the room and the situation's fairly heavily reliant on the vet coming up with a solution.

Lisa is trained in emergency veterinary medicine and, because she works at SASH, she sees a lot more emergency cases than I do. When I asked her if she'd find it hard to be in a 'normal' clinic after doing so much emergency work, she not surprisingly said, 'Yes. When you're used to dealing with these high-adrenaline-rush cases, it would be hard to vaccinate pets and do simple procedures. But then I look at the other side of it and think it would be nice to see healthy animals. In emergency work you never really see healthy animals – all the animals are sick with something. It might be nice once in a while to vaccinate a healthy puppy and talk about worming.'

Maybe balance is the key. Certainly I don't ever want to stop doing emergency cases – I'd like to try to be good in all the different areas of vet practice.

Not long after losing Jackie, I get another chance to put my emergency skills to the test when Natan brings in his labrador, Cody.

Like Jackie, Cody has come off second best in a collision with a car; apparently he saw Natan's son, Brendon, across the street and bolted down the stairs of the family home and onto the road.

Cody is sporting some visible reminders of his encounter: long, black tyre marks. He also has a haemorrhage around the eyes and his heart rate is very high, most probably because of the stress. The rate of oxygenation in his blood is lower than it should be – ninety-three or ninety-four per cent when it should be at least ninety-six per cent. His breathing certainly isn't great and he's panting a little bit, so I just need to stabilise that with some oxygen and try to calm him down with some medication as well. I also have to consider that his lowered oxygenation may indicate internal bleeding – possibly a ruptured blood vessel in his abdomen or lungs. I'll need to watch him closely over the next hour or so.

Cody is plucky, though. He also has youth on his side, is solid, like a lot of labradors – and he also has a lot of love. Natan's son and daughter, Brendon and Lara, are on the phone trying to say hello to their little mate. I can hear the quaver in Brendon's voice; Natan tells me that his son is a bit 'emotional'. I can only imagine how it would feel to watch your beloved pet being run over and feel responsible – so this isn't a big surprise. Brendon promises Cody a treat if he gets better and comes home. Lara, his younger sister, is a bit more pragmatic about the whole situation; curiously, she wants to know if I'm fat. Not something I have been asked much when treating a family pet! I can't help but laugh . . . Maybe she's drawing a picture of the scene at home and just wants to get the proportions right? Who knows what is going through her mind. All I want to know is . . . what if I was?

Between Natan in the clinic and the kids on the other end of the phone, it's a reminder of how the human emotions involved in an emergency can be just as strong as the animal's. This time, I think they're in luck. Cody's tail just keeps wagging and after an hour or so in the treatment room I'm satisfied that there is no internal bleeding. His blood oxygen levels are fine, there are no fractures and no obvious signs of concussion or brain-swelling, so I give the okay for him to go home. I can't help but think sadly of Jackie as I do. If only every case came out the right way.

Cody's remarkable recovery adds a little weight to a theory I've got about labradors – nothing worries them. And I have a theory as to why.

Labradors are popular family pets, and it's not hard to understand: they're good-natured – it would be highly unusual to see them get nippy with anyone – and they are well-known as guide and assistance dogs, thus giving most people the impression that they're a cut above your average pooch.

It's true that labradors are incredibly focused on learning – for the simple fact that it gets them food. They'll do anything to learn. But make no mistake: they would sell their owners for a lump of liver because they are *that* obsessed by it. And it's this that makes them very easy to train. An easily trainable dog seems like a winner to humans – and this is why labradors have gained this reputation for being intelligent. But I'm not so sure this is a truly well-earned award.

How Intelligent is Your Dog?

The most respected voice in the field of animal intelligence, Dr Stanley Coren, a neuropsychologist and Professor of Psychology from the University of British Columbia in the US, believes that three factors make a pet 'intelligent' . . .

1. **Problem-solving ability** Confronted with a situation like a bowl of food behind a closed door, does a dog stand there and wait for the door to open, or attempt to get around the current obstacle by rushing around the outside of the house to see if another door is open to ensure he/she gets the food before anyone else does?

2. **Instinctive intelligence** Instinct is a powerful influence on the way our pets think. Those who can harness their instinctive urges most effectively will often earn the biggest rewards. For example, a pet comes across a room containing two treats. The first is small but just one metre in front of it. However, sitting just half a metre behind it is a treat three times as large. Not knowing how long the pet has before another hungry animal might arrive, does it spend time eating the smaller treat and then move on to the much larger one, or maximise its returns and go straight for the

bigger reward and then come back to the smaller one if it has time . . . The most 'intelligent' pet should take the biggest reward first.

3. **Learning ability** Just as in people, some of our pets' minds absorb information more readily than others'. An animal's ability to then use that information to their advantage is what marks the most intelligent from the least intelligent. For an animal who is desperate for a walk, being able to realise when a potential opportunity for exercise is presenting itself is invaluable. Hence, a smart pet will see when its owner is putting their favourite joggers on and make their presence felt, thereby increasing their chances of a walk.

As you can see from what makes an intelligent pet, they are all qualities that can't be taught. Your pet is born intelligent . . . or not . . . whatever the case may be!

Ranks 1 to 10: Brightest Dogs

Understanding of New Commands: less than 5 repetitions.
Obey First Command: 95% of the time or better.

1. Border Collie
2. Poodle
3. German Shepherd
4. Golden Retriever

5. Doberman Pinscher
6. Shetland Sheepdog
7. Labrador
8. Papillon
9. Rottweiler
10. Australian Cattle Dog

Ranks 70 to 79: Lowest Degree Working Dogs/Lowest Obedience and Intelligence

Understanding of New Commands: 80 to 100 repetitions or more.

Obey First Command: 25% of the time or worse.

70. Shih Tzu
71. Basset Hound
72. Mastiff/Beagle
73. Pekingese
74. Bloodhound
75. Borzoi
76. Chow Chow
77. Bulldog
78. Basenji
79. Afghan Hound

Source: Dr Stanley Coren, *The Intelligence of Dogs*
(Free Press, New York, 1996).

What about the intelligence of . . .

Cats

- Cats are more difficult to assess.
- They have a very high level of 'sensory' intelligence – they are 'in-tune' with their senses and what the messages mean.
- Cats' perceived intelligence is based more on a sensory awareness and use of instinct.
- They tend to have rare periods of high mental activity (hunting, evasion, feeding) with up to twenty hours of low mental activity (like sleep) taking up the major part of their day.

Birds

- Birds are highly intelligent.
- They need constant stimulation to occupy very active minds.
- They have good problem-solving ability.
- Birds are skilled mimics.
- They recognise people, shapes, sound extremely well.
- Birds have strong memory capacity.
- The larger parrots (for example, Sun Conure, African Grey, Cockatoo and the Macaw) tend to be the most intelligent.

11

Felix the Kitten

While I am dealing with Cody and giving his family the good news, over at SASH Lisa is dealing with the sort of case I dread: a young cat – still a kitten, really, at five months of age – presenting with a whole range of symptoms that all add up to a potentially very bad situation. The kitten's name is Felix and his owner, Hazel, is beside herself with worry.

'Felix was absolutely fine until yesterday,' says Hazel, 'and then this morning he didn't eat his breakfast, and he was really down. He's usually a lively little kitten. And his skin was all dry, and then he started retching and vomiting and had diarrhoea and just became really floppy.'

Lisa examines him and notes that he is 'in pain. Cats are normally very stoic animals and he's yelping out when I'm feeling his abdomen, so he's in a lot of pain. It's possible that he could have swallowed something. He's a young cat and kittens play with anything. They ingest lots of different things. I can't feel anything obvious there. I just hope it's something that we can fix.'

Felix also has a high fever – it is forty-one degrees Celsius.

When Lisa puts these two pieces of information together she knows it could indicate a number of different problems, Felix could have a kidney infection or possibly pancreatitis. But the greatest worry for her (and Felix) is that he has FIP – Feline Infectious Peritonitis – which is a fatal condition. That is, of course, the worst-case scenario, but because of how the cat is presenting Lisa has to rule it in before she can rule it out.

FIP is caused by a virus. The original virus mutates and that mutation becomes a more lethal form that results in FIP. 'Peritonitis' means inflammation of the peritoneum, which is the lining of the abdominal cavity and also the lining of certain organs in the abdomen. This inflammation causes pain, which Felix is obviously experiencing, but there could be a number of other reasons for a cat to have abdominal pain – pancreatitis, a bowel obstruction or something causing severe wind, or an intestinal infection or tear. Certainly, Lisa is hoping it's one of these, but Felix's age is giving her more reason, not less, to think it's FIP: FIP occurs in young cats who pick up the virus in catteries at the breeders, and the full force of the condition doesn't reveal itself until the cats are a few months old. By that time the owners have become attached to their new family member, and as the disease often appears in pure-bred kittens, the owners are losing a pedigree cat that they've paid quite a bit of money for: they have reason to be upset on a number of fronts.

If Felix does have FIP and it is allowed to progress, his brain and lungs will start to be affected. Although there is no real treatment for the disease, there are antiviral therapies which have varying degrees of success, but none of these lead to a cure. Such treatments only prolong the cat's life, but the longest the animal could live would be one year, two at the most. Most typically, the prognosis is anywhere from a few weeks to months.

So you can see why Lisa is especially anxious about Felix's condition. Because SASH has an ultrasound machine and a cat specialist, they see a lot of FIP cases – and it's Lisa's familiarity with the symptoms that is leading her closer and closer to the diagnosis. Everything seems to be pointing this way, but all Lisa can do is run some tests and cross her fingers that Felix has more lives to live.

Most of SASH's cases come from referrals from clinics like the one I work in at Bondi. As Lisa explains, 'Because SASH is a specialist hospital, the animals have to be referred. For us it's an issue of managing cases that other vets feel they don't want to manage anymore or don't have the facilities to manage, or if the animal needs twenty-four-hour supervision and they don't offer such care at their practice.'

Felix was referred to SASH by his usual vet who, like Lisa, suspected FIP and knew SASH was better equipped to diagnose the disease. It's just as well for Felix – he's going to need the close care that only SASH can offer.

12

Pups in Prison

Since I graduated as a vet I haven't always practised in Sydney and surfed every day at Bondi. I am very lucky that my job has taken me to some remarkable places. I have moved around a bit: from my rural placement days on remote properties in New South Wales, to remote Aboriginal communities in the deserts of the Northern Territory and also to the out-of-the-way places that harbour distressed wildlife. I have been fortunate to get out of my comfort zone and learn a great deal from these experiences. And then, of course, I am still constantly making house calls and visiting the homes of people I don't know.

So when it's time for me to make a house call with a difference, to Kirkconnell Correctional Institution in central New South Wales, you'd think I'd take it in my stride. But, to be honest, I get a bit nervous on the long, rainy drive out there. I am not sure why I'm feeling this way. Maybe because I'm going to be inside an institution that most of us hope never to visit. Or maybe it's just the fact that I'm going to be treating three animals at once – and they're all labradors. And with rationed food in correctional centres, who knows how they would be behaving?

In 2004 I became an ambassador for Assistance Dogs Australia (ADA). ADA trains dogs – usually labradors, for the reasons I mentioned in the previous chapter – to live with and assist people confined to a wheelchair. They are different from guide dogs, which help blind people only. Assistance dogs can turn lights on and off, open doors and pick up things from the floor; basically, anything that is difficult or impossible for someone in a wheelchair to do. Like guide dogs, they make great companions for their owners. Assistance dogs are provided free of charge to the owner by the ADA, but demand exceeds supply so there is a long waiting list for the service.

I am very proud to be involved with such a worthwhile charity and as part of my role as an ambassador I provide veterinary care for as many of the dogs as I can; occasionally I'll be called on to make sure a dog is physiologically sound to either commence or continue in a training program. It's always amazing to see these puppies progressing through their training, but because of the good work they do and the constant demand for fully-trained assistance dogs, there is always a need for more trainers, which is why I'm headed to Kirkconnell.

A few years ago Kirkconnell started a program to reward some of its most trusted inmates: a handful of them were selected to train assistance dogs and they were assigned a puppy to live with them in the jail. These men are completely responsible for their dog for the duration of the eighteen-month training period.

The Kirkconnell program is part of a broader initiative within ADA: Pups in Prison, which was launched in November 2002 with the support of the New South Wales Department of Justice. Apart from Kirkconnell, two other prisons in New South Wales, the Darling Downs and Junee Correctional Centres, also host puppies. Of the ADA dogs in training at any given time, approximately one-quarter are pups in prison. Kirkconnell was the first prison to trial the program, and its initial success prompted the expansion to these two other jails. Five businesses in the area around Kirkconnell also became involved, providing building equipment and labour to construct the kennels and a compound needed for the dogs. Community support and involvement has been crucial to the ongoing success of the program.

In the New South Wales Parliament in 2004, then New South Wales Minister for Justice John Hatzistergos stated, 'The purposes of the Prison Pups Program and the involvement of inmates in it are the development of a sense of responsibility in the selected inmates, to enable inmates to acquire skills in pet care, the provision of appropriate pet care strategies, and the utilisation of inmates in the construction and ongoing maintenance of the facilities at Kirkconnell. This collaboration has demonstrated that correctional centres and the community can work together to provide valuable community-focused programs that benefit persons who would not normally have the support or resources necessary to ensure their independence.'*

I believe the Prison Pups Program is a very worthwhile initiative, and so here I am about to literally get the 'inside' word on it.

Upon arriving at Kirkconnell I go through security screening and then I am introduced to the trainers, Mark, Bill and Andrew, and their dogs Yoshi, Yogi and Ziggy. Mark has been in jail for twenty-one years; Andrew, though still a young man, has been in and out of jail several times. I didn't hear Bill's story, and I was reluctant to ask. While we are together we all share one aim; I don't want to dwell on the past negatives when what these three men are involved in is so positive. What matters to me is that all the men now have the same story: they're completely committed to their dogs. Their three pups are playful and healthy, and clearly doted on by their trainers. During the day the animals have lots of space in which to run around and at night the dogs sleep in the same room as their trainer.

I am here to assess the dogs' health, so I start with the basics by checking their toenails, which are pretty worn down; there's obviously no life of leisure for these labs.

'They must get plenty of exercise,' I say to Bill.

'They dig a lot of holes,' he replies, smiling.

---

* *Source*: NSW Hansard 9 March 2004 http://www.parliament.nsw. gov.au

'They're not trying to dig out of here, are they?'

'Ha!' says Bill. 'I never thought of that one.'

'You could be onto something there,' I say, laughing.

'Shhhh,' Bill says with a grin, 'there are officers over there.'

The puppies are typically lively as I try to keep them still long enough to check them over. I don't need to linger long to register the fact that they are clearly very healthy and happy. It is obvious to me that Mark, Bill and Andrew are doing a great job. But I need to be sure, so I take my time to talk to each man and assess each animal.

When I chat to Mark about the training program, he tells me he wanted to be a part of it because his dog, Yoshi, will end up 'going to help out some poor bugger in a wheelchair. And that's who I'm looking to help – make life better for somebody in a wheelchair.

'Yoshi is my mate,' he continues. 'It means a great deal – I can't put it into words.'

Unlike humans, the dogs can't and don't judge their trainers for being in prison. To the dogs the men are owners, companions, friends – people they trust and believe in. The dogs and their trainers can really lean on each other and have a great bond – with no conditions attached.

'The feeling is stupendous,' says Mark. 'It has me glowing inside. I really feel now that I'd be lost if I didn't see Yoshi for a day or two.'

However, not all the dogs who go through the training program will end up becoming assistance dogs. The ones that don't make it could become companion dogs or just much-loved pets.

Sometimes, even after eighteen months of training and lots of love and care from the trainer, a dog is just not suited to the job. Mainly it's because of their temperament and their ability to focus on a task. Occasionally, a physical problem rules them out. And that's what's concerning me as I carefully examine Mark's dog, Yoshi.

Mark tells me that Yoshi has been limping for a few days, mainly in the mornings. As I can see the dogs play fairly roughly with each other, there's a chance that it's just a sprain – and that's the diagnosis I would be hoping for. The worst diagnosis would be elbow dysplasia, a developmental joint condition that is common in large-breed dogs. If Yoshi had this it would rule him out of the program and, no doubt, completely devastate Mark. I will need to examine the puppy further to work out what's going on.

If you have a pet, you'll know how much they enrich your life and how much joy they can bring. Pets can give unconditional love – particularly dogs, although sometimes they just love us because we feed them – and they can also teach us about ourselves. Humans who find it difficult to relate to other humans can learn how to care for others by caring for their pet; the animal's ability to love them unquestioningly can give them faith in themselves where previously there was none. There are lots of stories about how animals have changed people's lives for the better.

I can't imagine life without my own dog, Rusty. Rusty, who's a kelpie, came from a farm adjacent to my parents' property near Stroud in New South Wales. He was a nervous little thing – not very trusting of humans – and in need of some serious, dedicated attention if he was to improve. Several years later I'm happy to say that he's a lot better than he used to be, even if he is still a bit shy of strangers. He's my little mate and I wouldn't be without him.

So I understand the effect that Yoshi, Ziggy and Yogi could have on their trainers. Not only that, but I can see it on the faces of the men whenever they talk about their dogs. Regardless of how they came to be in jail, there can be no doubt that their idea of themselves is affected by the fact that they are inmates. And jail doesn't really provide a lot of opportunities for them to change that perception – unlike the outside world, there are no mountains to climb or promotions to earn. Working with these dogs provides Andrew, Mark and Bill with the chance to achieve something – and not just for themselves. They are all aware that the dogs they're training will, hopefully, go on to make life easier for people in wheelchairs. Their role in that process is something of which they're justifiably proud. If the dogs have helped them to realise that they contribute something to the world, then that's an amazing achievement.

Cathie Turner, one of the prison officers at Kirkconnell, tells me she's thrilled at the way the training program has turned out – it is, she says, beyond their expectations. The whole jail benefits from having the dogs there as they bring joy to so many. And the dogs, too, are lucky to be placed with trainers who are so careful about their program and welfare.

I manipulate Yoshi's front left leg so I can hopefully determine whether this is a simple injury or whether there's an underlying condition which is causing his limp. If it's the latter, I really don't want to be the one to tell Mark that his new best friend will have to leave the program – and him.

Elbow dysplasia is – like the more common hip dysplasia – a genetic condition which means that the animal's elbow joint has developed poorly and is now misshapen and a source of pain. In severe cases – the bones in the elbow joint can even slip out. So it is with some fear that I feel my way down his leg, flexing and extending each joint to see if there is any response. When I get to the elbow I'm surprised – there's no pain or stiffness. A great result. When I manipulate his wrist he winces when I flex it. So that's where our problem is. Obviously I don't like causing pain to animals, but in this case it's an indicator that he most likely has only a sprain, which is treatable with rest and anti-inflammatory medication. I'm relieved for Mark.

Since Yoshi is staying in the program, he can now accompany Mark, Andrew and Ziggy to a local primary school where the men are going to talk about how they train the dogs, and the dogs are going to get dozens of pats and cuddles from the children. Astonishingly, this will be the first time Mark has left the prison in twenty-one years – and the first time he's been in a car since he started his sentence. And it turns out sometimes the simplest things can be the source of the greatest amazement. His fascination with the car's electric windows is a big surprise. Then there are the flashing lights and buttons of the car's stereo system. And don't start him on the fact the car can play CDs. It really reminds me how much most of us take for granted. He looks like a child on Christmas morning, and his sense of wonder at the world around him makes me realise why he's such a good person to train Yoshi. Everything about Yoshi interests him; as a result he's unlikely to get bored with the program.

On the drive over, Mark and Andrew talk nervously about the school visit.

'I hope Yoshi goes all right,' says Mark. 'I hope he's not too frightened and intimidated by the children.'

'It will be good to see how they go with the kids, actually,' Andrew responds, and Mark nods, smiling all the while. 'The kids will all want to get in there and touch the pups. It'll be good.'

In the back seat, the dogs seem to bark their agreement.

This is the third group of trainee assistance dogs to visit the school, and there's a lot of excitement among the students.

'They just love them,' says Trish Forsyth, the principal of Meadow Flat Primary School, 'and they love the boys bringing them down. We're now in the process of trying to organise sponsorship of one of the pups in the program.

'They're always very polite,' says Trish of the inmates, 'and always very concerned about the children and doing the right thing in the school.'

With the audience's rapt attention, Mark tries to get Yoshi to 'speak' on command – it doesn't work straightaway, but Yoshi does let out a little bark and gets his reward. Mark and Andrew talk about their dogs and patiently answer the children's many questions, before disappearing in a mob of school uniforms when the children descend on the dogs, who are remarkably unflustered by all the attention. I try to warn the kids about overwhelming the dogs, but I have a suspicion that absolutely no one is going to listen to me when there are two cute labradors in the room.

Although I should have known that kids will be kids – I was hoping the question wouldn't be asked. But surely enough as we were finishing up, Nathan, a freckled red-headed kid sitting in the front row asked Andrew, 'Why are you in prison?'

Just as I was about to jump in and create a diversion, Andrew calmly replied, 'Library books, kids. Always return your library books,' as he winked at me in acknowledgment of a situation saved.

Afterwards, Mark says that the whole experience was 'precious – you can't put a price on that. I know the children love the dogs and because of that it made me feel good.'

'It was like a father with his son,' says Andrew of his own experience, 'at the first football game when he scores his first try.'

The trip was special for me, too. The easy interaction between Mark, Andrew and the kids is another example of the special gifts that animals give to humans: they can help us bridge any divide.

13

A Good
News Day

The tests on Felix, the young cat being treated at SASH, are not giving Lisa any reassurance that the kitten is suffering from something other than FIP. His blood test results show that his white cell count is elevated at thirty-five; the upper end of normal is under twenty. The reading indicates an inflammation of the organs – another marker that could mean FIP, which attacks the entire abdominal area. An ultrasound is needed to work out what's really going on.

Before Lisa can attend to that, however, there's an emergency – a Maltese terrier called Bianca goes into heart failure. Just like a scene in a human hospital, a cluster of vets and nurses surrounds the table the dog has been placed on, working quickly to prevent her from dying. It's as tense a situation as any vet would face. As Lisa says, 'There's not much talking. Everyone works on autopilot. You know what you have to do and it's got to be done quickly if you want to get the results.'

Thankfully, Bianca pulls through. Once everyone's adrenaline levels have settled, they can get back to the other animals, including Felix.

Lisa and fellow vet Darren Foster – who is a Feline Medicine specialist at SASH – give Felix his ultrasound. They are looking for signs of inflammation – any free fluid, enlarged lymph nodes or abnormalities in any of the organs. They're also going to have a look at the pancreas and the kidneys to make sure they're not both inflamed. If there is only one swollen organ, then they can rule out FIP.

Lisa holds her breath as the image appears on the screen. As Darren moves the ultrasound over Felix's abdomen, he can see that only the pancreas is inflamed. This indicates that his condition is most likely pancreatitis – inflammation of the pancreas. This can be caused by bacteria that get in from the bowel or from sudden dietary changes – or 'dietary indiscretions', as Darren says, such as eating mice.

It is a good result for Felix, and Lisa can now send him home with some antibiotics and pain relief, and an instruction to Hazel for Felix to drink lots of fluids. Lisa is very pleased to be able to tell his owner that her beloved pet should be fine in a few days.

Being a vet has as many highs and lows as being a doctor for humans. This has been a good day – for Felix, for his owner, Hazel, and for Lisa and the team at SASH. There are bad days, too. Days when a cat *will* have FIP. Days when we have to tell owners that their beloved pet needs to be put down. And days when I simply shake my head in dismay at what some people will do to their animals. On the balance, there are more good days – it's just a shame that the bad ones seem to leave more lasting impressions.

14

An
Urban Vet

Becoming a vet in Australia takes quite a long time – and that is if you can get into the course. There are only five universities in the whole of the country (The University of Queensland, The University of Sydney, The University of Melbourne, Charles Sturt University and Murdoch University) that offer a degree in veterinary science, so if you want to become a vet and you don't live near one of those universities you have to move, which offers its own challenges. I did my degree at the University of Sydney and, as Sydney wasn't home at that time, I moved away from my family to study. I was lucky that I had their support.

The degree itself takes five years, and while students in a medicine degree only have to study one type of body – human – vets have to know all the intricacies of many different types of bodies and their systems. In order for us to be effective in our jobs we have to know about dogs, cats, birds of all sorts, horses, cows, sheep, goats, rabbits, frogs, fish, lizards, snakes, kangaroos . . . Well, you get the idea. In fact, thinking about it this way makes it surprising that the degree isn't longer! While in my fifth year I was glad it's not – you're well aware of just how much you have had to learn!

It's common for students to take jobs in veterinary clinics while they are studying; in my Bondi clinic we have three students who live upstairs and act as the overnight on-call service. This is a great way for them to learn not only how to treat animals, but also how a city clinic really works – being a vet is definitely not a nine-to-five job; we have to be available to treat emergencies if they come in during the night. But the reality is that it's hard to get cranky at an animal if it *is* injured or ill during the night, plus this work is often the most rewarding.

Each vet student has to do some form of work experience – or 'prac', as it is commonly called – on a rural property as well as a city clinic, so they get the chance to work with all different sorts of animals. The biggest focus during a rural prac is working with large animals such as horses and cows. It is here that you discover that this work is as much a physical challenge as it is a mental one.

Many students aren't as lucky as me to have this opportunity before they study at uni. When you're doing your rural prac, there are two sections of work: non-veterinary and veterinary. I know it sounds a little strange, but much of a student's time is spent just experiencing the working life on a farm so they can appreciate what's important to farmers and how they look after their animals. It can be disappointing at first, not being involved in hands-on vet work every minute, but it is almost as important.

Because of my background I was already familiar with large animals. I've got to say I like working with them just as much as smaller, domestic animals. I am not exactly sure why, but I do like the physical challenge of large animals – the fact that they really make you work hard and you have to be on your game or they can push you around makes for a very different experience from working with their smaller counterparts.

I especially love working with cattle. I've loved cows since I was a child. For my twelfth birthday I pestered my parents, and promised to go without future birthday and Christmas gifts to ensure that I got a cow for my present. To my surprise, they gave in and gave me a Jersey – a quiet and calm breed that's also great for milking.

Once I had one, I was very keen on the idea of creating my own dairy cow empire so I bred my cow – over and over again. She produced nine male calves in a row, which is some kind of freakish run that I've never heard of or seen since. Now, it *was* fantastic that she was so good at breeding – but you can't milk a male. I kept the first four or five calves, because I really couldn't bear to let them go, but then it became too costly for my parents to look after all those non-milk-giving, non-beef-giving cattle on their farm, so I had to sell the rest. I remember speaking to those first few calves as soon as they were born and promising them I'd look after them and wouldn't sell them, but I had to stop saying anything after a while because I knew I couldn't keep my word. Despite giving birth so many times, that first Jersey cow lived until she was twenty-two years old – in fact she only died a few years ago.

One of the great challenges about being a vet is staying on top of everything I learned at university. I may not see a penguin very often, for example, but I have to be able to treat one if a case presents itself. I also don't treat nearly as many large animals as I'd like – it was the one thing I had to sacrifice when I decided to stay in Sydney. To be honest, the trade-off was the beach: I could treat large animals or I could still treat an interesting and amazing array of animals, but also squeeze in a surf nearly every morning. The surf won and I haven't regretted that choice. But I still love to be around farm animals, so I jump at any chance to treat them.

Lady the goat is one of the many animals living a nice bucolic life in the grounds of historic Vaucluse House in Sydney. The clinic received a call from the caretaker there, telling us that Lady's hooves were overgrown and that she was having trouble walking properly. It sounded to me like she needed a manicure.

If only it were that easy . . .

In order to clip Lady's toenails, I have to catch her first. She may be a geriatric in animal terms, but she really gives me a run for it. The most recent day I visited her I really should have skipped my morning surf, because I needed all my energy just to run her down. Eventually a flying tackle did the trick – not that tackling an old 'Lady' gives me kicks – there's just no other way of doing it!

Once I finished the job – still with no holes nibbled in my shirt – Lady immediately sprang off around the enclosure in which I'd corralled her. For an old girl she's certainly very lively, and it's good to see that overgrown hooves were her only hindrance. A goat living on a farm will generally walk over rougher terrain than a goat with Lady's suburban lifestyle on manicured lawns, and that helps to keep the hooves at a manageable level. Any hoofed animals living in the city need to be monitored to make sure the same thing doesn't happen to them. Lady will also have to be given arthritis tablets – these particular tablets are meant for dogs but are perfectly okay for goats – and she'll be given them in her favourite food: green beans.

While I'm at Vaucluse House I also check on an old friend. Mercedes the chicken, who used to call my place home. I grew up to the sound of chooks in the back garden and so for a while when I moved to Bondi I kept two. I love the noise they make and I certainly liked the free-range eggs. Eventually I realised the clucking and calling noises I loved might not have the same soothing effect for my neighbours so I said goodbye to the chooks and Mercedes came to live in Vaucluse.

I don't see many chickens at the clinic – we had a stray chicken wander in once, and we had no idea where it came from, but that was my last poultry patient. So I don't have any opportunities to practise my special chicken-hypnotising trick. As Mercedes was always one of my best subjects, I decide to try it out on her while I'm here.

My three-step guide to hypnotising chickens is first, to lie them down on their back; second, tuck their chin down towards their chest; and third, stroke them on the chest, lightening your touch over a minute until you're barely touching them at all. From there they should remain placidly poised on their back until you wake them up. And, sure enough, Mercedes is the perfect subject: she is out straightaway and she doesn't come to until I rouse her.

I don't really know what purpose it serves. It's basically just a party trick, and most people think it's a good one! And while I'm hypnotising Mercedes it gives me more time to rest after chasing Lady!

Given my fondness for farm animals, I was delighted to receive an invitation to be the official vet at the Stroud show. I took my dog Rusty along with me so he could visit his old home. Many Australian country towns have annual shows; they provide an opportunity for townsfolk and people living on outlying properties to get together and celebrate their community. They also serve the practical purposes of allowing farmers to show their wares in competition with each other – there are prizes for cows, bulls, vegetables and other things. Stroud also boasts some very special events that are unique to Australian country shows, but shared with other towns named Stroud in the United Kingdom, United States of America and New Zealand: a rolling pin and brick-throwing competition. I know it is stereotyping, but it is tradition: women get to throw rolling pins for distance, and men throw bricks. I'm not quite sure why men can't throw rolling pins too, but the rules are the rules.

As the official vet I am light on the 'vet' and heavy on the 'official' – I present prizes for animals who win their various divisions.

It's very different from a show like the Sydney Royal Easter Show or the Brisbane Ekka, but I like that difference. In one event there were just two cows competing against each other, so it's safe to say they both had a fair chance of a ribbon.

At the rodeo there are no ribbons but lots of cracked ribs. Several cowboys – 'maniacs' may be a better term – take their turns riding bucking bulls who outweigh them twenty to one. I'm left wondering why there's an official vet for this show but, apparently, no official doctor . . .

This particular day the vet part only kicks in when I receive a call from Juliet Clark, who, with her husband, runs a dairy farm with both Guernsey and Friesian cows, not far from town. I had actually done some of my rural prac there so know the Clarks well. Juliet knew I was going to be in town so she calls to see if I can help her out. I'm happy to.

One of her cows is in labour and it has been going on too long. She thinks there's a chance the calf is stuck. This is never a great prospect – it's bad enough when human babies get stuck, but at least they only have two legs and only weigh a few kilos! Trying to haul out a four-legged creature of considerable size and weight is quite a challenge.

Many farmers, for simple economic reasons, will avoid calling a vet out if they can possibly avoid it. Most of those that I know are experienced in delivering young animals so it is completely the norm that a vet is only contacted for those they're having trouble with, like when cows that are lying down can't give birth because of calving paralysis, when the calf is backwards or if there is a chance it's twins. Sometimes a calf will have one leg pulled back and you can't get it out, because the hind leg is stuck, so you have to push it forward.

The Clarks' cow hasn't been able to push out her calf on her own, and once the calf's feet show there is only about ten or twenty minutes to get it out before there's a chance that the animal will die of oxygen deprivation. When I arrive at the farm, time is very much of the essence, so much so that I can't stop to change into the overalls I usually wear to deliver large animals. Trust me, the overalls are needed! Delivering the young of a large animal is very physical work and very, very messy. If I had forgotten this, it isn't long before I am reminded.

It has been a year or so since I last delivered a calf, but I have to snap into action fast.

I plunge one hand in and try to form a mental image of what the calf is doing and what position it is in. The first things I am searching for are the feet, as they will tell me if the calf is the right way up or upside down. If a calf is upside down there's usually a prolonged period of silence

– a moment where I try to hide my true feelings, which often involve swear words of some sort – and this doesn't normally go down so well with the farmers, who are now looking even more concerned. I then feel for the head to see if it's on top or at the side. Thankfully the Clark calf is right-side up, but there is still a bit of a knack to getting it out. I can't pull the animal out in a straight line – it needs to come at a slight downward angle. A perfect delivery always ends up being a little bit like doing hand gymnastics inside the mother – goodness knows what she thinks is going on!

I tie some rope around the calf's forelegs – it feels not unlike trying to tie my shoelaces in the dark, and all the while the cow's body and the calf are moving and pushing my hands away from where they should be. The calf also seems to be quite large. So, here goes . . .

With a few pulls I enter myself in a rather one-way game of tug of war. After much struggling, I whip out the calf as best I can, as the amniotic fluid and blood goes all over my shirt, pants and shoes. The calf weighs about forty-five or fifty kilograms; however, because it's slimy and limp, it feels more like a hundred kilos. So it's a bit like carrying a very heavy lump of warm butter – if I get slightly off balance it will slide out of my hands. I'm mindful of not dropping it on its head and try to cushion its fall. It still hits with a thud, although it doesn't seem to mind. If the calf had been born in a field there would have been no one there to catch it.

As soon as the newborn's on the ground I try to get all the mucous out of its mouth and then annoy it a little bit, which stimulates its nerves so all its sensations come to life. This then triggers a breath – and that's the breath I'm waiting for. Now I can check to see whether it's a boy or a girl; it's female, and she's a beauty.

Juliet will never say it, but she'd be absolutely thrilled that it's a girl. Around the farm male calves are of no use whatsoever. After all, what's that saying about being useless and a bull? This is a dairy farm. It's the females that produce the milk, and the Clarks rely on the milk to make any money. You don't get much milk out of a male.

The cow shortly moves over to meet her newborn, and their dialogue begins almost immediately; Mum grunts at her calf, then she nudges her and gives her a lick. It's a process that I always find amazing – they're bonding without talking, but they are communicating, and there is immediate recognition. Animals are able to connect so quickly that they put humans to shame, in a way. Moreover, human babies are born and we can nurse them for years, whereas calves need to be born and walking that day. And, sure enough, Juliet comes to take the cow back to the milking shed and I carry the calf to the nursery, where she takes her first hesitant steps. Her name is Ivanhoe Zing – after her father and mother – a name that would put a glitterati Hollywood baby to shame – yet this calf is about as far from LA as possible! It's a tough moment; Mum is leaving the calf after she's carried her for nine months and then it's over so quickly. But that's farm life – it's very real. I could sit and watch this all day, but Rusty's waiting in the car – and my clothes desperately need to be changed.

I've delivered the young of almost every major species. Apart from stillbirths it is always an awesome experience, and great fun. Normally when I'm operating and doing something so physical, it's to correct a problem; when I'm assisting at a birth I'm not correcting a problem but inducing a solution. Instead of having a wounded animal at the end, we end up with a fresh new one. It is a privilege to be able to do this work. It's a good thing I feel that way, because I don't expect a gush of appreciation from Juliet. She has been on the land for years and is as tough as they come. After delivering Ivanhoe Zing alive and well, I think I'm entitled to think I've done okay. But Juliet disagrees. 'It could have been quicker.' Juliet is about five feet tall on the old scale – quite a lot shorter than me – and she weighs about the same as a newborn calf herself, but I'm pretty sure that if there had been no problems with the birth she would have delivered it quicker; she knows cows better than almost anyone I know. But despite not quite meeting Juliet's expectations I still feel great as I pack away my calf-delivering skills for another year.

15

A Drowned Cat

As a vet in a local clinic I see pet owners who care about their animals. Most owners look after their pets well, and by 'well' I don't mean that they buy their Alsatian trimmed cuts of meat from the butcher or sardine fillets for their Burmese. The needs of a pet aren't so different from the needs of their owners: something to eat, somewhere to sleep, somewhere to stay dry and warm and to be loved. Ninety-nine point nine per cent of the owners I meet look after their animals, and that includes bringing them to us when they're sick or need a vaccination.

Because I usually only see these committed, kind owners, I sometimes forget that there are people in the world who can be unbelievably cruel to their pets. It is not something I like to dwell on. I'm sure you've seen reports on the news about people who fail to provide adequate food, water or veterinary care for their pets or keep them in small cages that are never cleaned. Those cases of extreme neglect are appalling. But I had one recent case that goes way beyond anything I've ever seen and I am hoping I never see anything like it again.

I received an evening call from Kelli and Germaine, the two vet students living above the clinic, letting me know that someone had seen a woman throwing a cage into the ocean pool at the southern end of Bondi. There was a cat in the cage. This pool, like many ocean baths in Australia, has waves constantly crashing into it at high tide, so it was no placid body of water. This cat was meant to drown.

The cage had been pulled out of the water by people at the scene and they called the police who then rushed it to the clinic. Kelly and Germaine immediately called me and I arrived not long after to a very sorry sight. This animal looked more like a sodden kitchen mop than a cat.

The water had been very cold and apparently the cat had sunk deep. It's both remarkable that it survived and horrendous that it had to survive this situation in the first place. I start to examine it and discover the cat – it seems a bit strange just to call it 'the cat' but I had no idea of its name – is battling hypothermia. I take its temperature and it is only thirty-two point seven degrees. It's meant to be between thirty-seven point five and thirty-nine degrees. I still can't believe this animal is alive. Of course I know the old adage about cats having nine lives but someone was intent on taking all nine of this cat's lives at once.

As soon as I've done a preliminary examination I can tell that I was right to be sceptical: its lungs are full of fluid and all I can hear are crackles. The cat has only sixty to seventy per cent of its lungs functioning. Probably one more inhalation in the water would have finished it off. Whoever rescued it did so with only seconds to spare.

I have to act fast if I am to make a difference to the outcome. I need to get direct access to its circulation so I can administer some drugs, otherwise shock could kill this cat. I set to work shaving one of its front legs so I can insert a needle.

He – I've discovered it's a he – must have been absolutely terrified. I can't begin to imagine what he must have been feeling as the water started to fill the cage. While cats may not have a human's capacity for rational thought, they can absolutely feel fear – it's an instinctive response for any warm-blooded creature. Given how close he came to losing his life, he must have been overwhelmed by terror. It is this, more than anything, that angers me about what's been done to this cat – that he had to feel this way and had no choice. How could anyone do this to him?

Kelli and Germaine bring out a hairdryer so they can dry the cat's fur and thus help to raise his body temperature further. He's in so much shock that I doubt he notices what's going on, but that means for the time being we can treat him more easily. It would be difficult if he were totally conscious to have the three of us working on him. Especially when I start to use cupping – literally making cups out of my hands, then tapping him around the lungs – working with gravity to try to force the fluid from them. The cat won't like it, but it's for his own good. And what we are doing is obviously helping as his temperature has risen a little to thirty-three point seven degrees.

Now I have seen this improvement in his core temperature my main concern is that he'll develop a lung infection or pneumonia from the salt water in his lungs. The truth is, I have never treated a cat that has nearly drowned before. It just doesn't happen. As a result, I can't predict what the outcome will be. For the moment, we've done as much as we can; the rest is up to him.

Once the cat's fur is completely dry, we set up a sleeping area for him, give him some antibiotics and something for the shock and wait to see what the rest of the night brings.

16

A New Start

What a difference a few hours make. The unresponsive wet mop that I first saw the evening before is now one very grumpy cat. He hisses at me from his cage and looks torn between moving as far away from me as possible and taking a swipe at my hand. I can't blame him – a human being did something unbelievably appalling to him. I wouldn't be surprised if this cat had trouble trusting any human ever again. At this point he doesn't even have confidence in the food we give him – and it's warm chicken!

After braving his swiping paw, the good news is that he is off the critical list: his vital signs are better and his lung function is improving – the capacity is back to ninety per cent. So while he may not win any Happy Cat awards in the immediate future, he has a shot at getting back to full strength.

I ask the vet nurse Sara if she's ever heard of anything like this case before.

'No,' she says, 'nothing like this. It's quite horrifying, actually. It's just a horrible thing to think of, that someone would throw a cat in the water in its cage . . . Hopefully we'll be able to get him a nice new home.'

Later that day we hear from the police that the cat's owner – perhaps not in her right mind – thought she was 'putting him out of his misery' when she threw him into the water. This suggests to me that she was horribly misguided and believed he was so ill that she had no other choice. The cat appears to me to have no underlying health problems apart from a bit of arthritis. If he had been ill, though, and his owner really felt she had no other choice, she could have brought him to us or taken him to any vet clinic and they would have euthanased him for her. There are always options when dealing with a sick animal and drowning a cat in a local sea pool should not ever be one that is considered.

While I don't know all the facts of this cat's case, I do believe the laws should be a lot stronger to punish people who hurt animals – there needs to be more of a deterrent for treating pets as if they're disposable. I'm all too aware that some people think that if it's not working out with a pet the first time, they should get rid of it and start again with another. This makes me furious. Pets are not toys or mobile phones. There's no money-back guarantee and there's no return to sender. Yes, they are a huge responsibility and, accordingly, people should always think carefully before getting a pet and make all the necessary preparations before the pet comes home. Laws that penalise people for treating animals like rubbish that can be dumped by the side of the road would, hopefully, encourage that kind of forethought and lead to less animals being dumped or treated cruelly. But ultimately, treating animals kindly isn't even something you should need laws for.

I keep the rescued cat at the clinic for a week. I am pleased at his recuperation and that there is no sign of the pneumonia I feared may result from his near-drowning. Though physically he continues to improve, that feisty streak I observed the morning after his incident remains. He is definitely one cranky cat. No doubt that's his protection mechanism – he doesn't want anyone to hurt him again.

We know that his owner probably won't be getting him back even if she wanted to, so we arrange for a foster carer, Julie, to look after him. When she arrives to pick him up Nurse Sara is sad to say goodbye. The truth is this cat has touched all of us with his tenacity and will to survive. But we know that Julie will take good care of him.

I've decided that we can't let the cat go without giving him a name. So I call him Huey – short for Houdini, after the great escape artist who I'm sure had an underwater escape that would rival our cat's! It seems fitting. Huey is a real character and he deserves a great home; I think he'll get that with Julie.

Huey seems to take to Julie straightaway – well, he doesn't try to swipe her so that is a great sign – and she looks very pleased to be looking after him. 'He needs a bit of time to settle,' she says. 'I think he's been tortured and traumatised. But I think he's going to make a beautiful, loving cat.' With Julie on the case I'm sure he's halfway there.

Foster Carers

Foster carers provide care in their own home at short notice for animals needing temporary housing until they can be reunited with their owner or permanently re-housed. Such volunteers prevent the unnecessary putting down of impounded animals.

How to become a foster carer:

- Ask at your local animal rescue centre for more information.

17

Flight Test

I've already mentioned the fact that vets take their responsibilities towards Australian fauna very seriously. I can't think of another country that has such a range of native animals that regularly come into close contact with humans and, therefore, are at an increased chance of being injured by them. In North America the native animals include bears, elk and wolves – and I suspect there wouldn't be many of them being taken to vet clinics if they'd been found by a concerned citizen on the side of the road.

Many of our native animals are quite small or, at least, of manageable size – the largest are the emu and the kangaroo – so we tend to think of our native animals as cute and, sometimes, cuddly. I guess you could say that Australians have a sentimental attachment to their wildlife, we celebrate how weird and wonderful they are and that's why we're more likely to care about what happens to them, to notice if an animal is injured and actually do something about it. As far as I know, there's no other country in the world where so many citizens have had contact with what are essentially wild animals, not just because of the nature of the animals but because there is so much wildlife in our cities. Sydney's harbour foreshores are largely classified as national park – they're bush, and there are native animals in them. There are kangaroos on suburban golf courses and in less densely populated parts of cities. Blue-tongue lizards and larger 'water dragons' can be found in urban gardens and although it's rare, koalas are even occasionally seen in their native habitat on city bushwalks.

I have probably had at least one of every wildlife species come through the clinic while I've been here. In fact, as I learned very early on, Bondi isn't only a dog and cat suburb! It's a great challenge for me. While these animals sometimes have pretty much the same physiology as domesticated animals, they often don't – after all, there's nothing like a platypus anywhere else in the world. I also just love treating them; I love that my job can encompass dogs, cats, cows, horses – and rainbow lorikeets.

Brian and his son Tom come into the clinic after finding an adult rainbow lorikeet in their back garden. The bird was almost breakfast for their dog – and by the very fact they could catch it, they concluded something wasn't quite right. They're spot on and really any bird that can't fly with its flock is an easy target for any cat or dog that stumbles across it. Native birds tend to travel in numbers, and somewhere around Brian and Tom's garden there will be a flock of lorikeets wondering what happened to their mate.

I start by examining the bird to try to work out what's going on. There are a number of possibilities. It could have flown into a window and ended up in their garden, or it could have picked up a condition that occurs in a lot of rainbow lorikeets called beak and feather disease. The bird is otherwise in good condition. Moving his wings around, I can see that they're not broken, and all his other bones seem to be fine. Most importantly, he seems to have all his feathers intact and accounted for!

Birds are tricky to treat because they're so fragile, and they're also great actors. They will hide any signs of sickness for as long as possible, until it's just too much for them. Essentially, if a bird is acting sick, the odds are it is almost in a critical condition. I will need to keep this little fellow around for a while, to see if his weakness and uncoordination continues.

I start him on some antibiotics, and he also needs to rest – which shouldn't be a problem in his current state, but we'll need to keep him in a cage to stop him exerting himself once the antibiotics kick in.

It is a busy day so I put him in a small cage out among the other animals we're keeping at the clinic. I figure he'll be safe there. And he is . . . for a few minutes. Then I hear Neil calling out to me – he's found the lorikeet on the ground and nowhere near his cage. Yes, it's a little embarrassing, but thankfully 'Laurie' hasn't done any damage to himself. Because basically this is my fault. You see, Laurie has done what many wildlife species are good at. Lulling me into a false sense of security by seeming so lethargic has made me think that even though those holes in the cage aren't that small there would be no chance he could squeeze through. Obviously I was wrong!

With what sounds like a well-deserved 'tsk-tsk', Neil whisks the lorikeet away to a more suitable abode.

The next day it's time for the lorikeet to have a test flight. If his inability to fly has been caused by a trauma or concussion such as flying into a window or being hit by a car, it should have worn off by now. If he still can't fly I think it is more likely that he is being affected by a virus.

The lorikeet makes a tentative solo venture across the room; as far as test flights go it's not too bad. But I'm not going to release him straightaway, for the simple fact that once he's released he's going to be very hard to catch again. And his strength just isn't up to surviving in the wild yet. But the signs are good so I am hopeful he'll make a full recovery.

He'll need a few more practice flights and for safety the clinic can be his practice aerodrome. Once he's able to fly decent distances – similar to those he'd travel in the wild – and he appears strong enough, I will be delighted to let him go.

Soon enough, after many test flights and constant feeding, the rainbow lorikeet is ready to leave us and I take him to a local park to be set free. As a thank you present, he bites me. There's no such thing as gratitude in the wildlife world but I figure if he is feisty enough to bite me he is obviously very keen to be on his way.

I launch the beautiful green and red bird into the air and he takes off like a rocket into the trees. I am pleased that, thanks to the care of Brian and Tom, along with the efforts of everyone at the clinic, this bird is back where he belongs.

Native birds are, along with possums, undoubtedly the most visible Australian wildlife in our cities. I'm sure you've seen cockatoos near your house – they are everywhere, and fearless with it. I think that fearlessness comes from their relentless pursuit of things to chew on – absolutely nothing can stop them getting to roof tiles, window seals and your newly blooming garden so they can tear it all to bits. They're magnificent creatures, so it's hard to stay mad at them – unless you encounter those shrieking cries early one Sunday morning when you're sporting a hangover.

18

Beanie

I have said before, my job is always varied and I never know what animal may turn up at the clinic on any given day. On one particularly memorable day a very small joey – a baby kangaroo – is brought in to the clinic by Leah from Sydney Wildlife, which is an organisation similar to WIRES. The little eastern grey had been found by a roadside, his mother dead, and the family who discovered him took him home. For three days they fed him cow's milk, and when his condition deteriorated they called Sydney Wildlife.

The joey is so newborn that he has no fur – he would have spent all of his life till now safely tucked up in his mother's pouch, where it would have been warm and well insulated, so he didn't need fur. Out here in the cold harsh world, though, he's suffering.

The cow's milk didn't help things, either. I am sure it is what many people in this situation would resort to but, sadly, it would have done more harm than good. Cow's milk is great for baby cows but its lactose content is a problem for a kangaroo – lactose is a sugar that kangaroos can't digest. So even though the family thought they were helping by feeding the orphaned joey it hasn't worked out that way and now the little guy is severely malnourished. If he'd arrived at my clinic twelve hours later, it would definitely have been too late. As it is, there is perhaps some small hope that we can keep this baby alive.

The bub was in a beanie when he arrived at the clinic, so we've decided to call him – what else – Beanie. Sara is on hand to help me look after him, and he's so adorable that everyone in the clinic has immediately fallen in love with him. We're really putting our hearts on the line, though, because this little guy is still very sick.

Leah from Sydney Wildlife shares my concerns. 'He hasn't been fed properly for three days,' she says, 'and normally in the pouch he'd be continuously getting nutrients and receiving warmth from his mother. So I don't think it's very good.'

I ask Sara for two ten-millilitre syringes of warm saline so I can get some fluids into the joey, who is cold and dehydrated, and quite possibly in shock as well.

I also give him a steroid injection which I hope will improve his circulation and generally give his systems a good boost, which he most definitely needs because everything seems to be crashing.

We feed him a special formula in an attempt to redress the malnourishment. This is a delicate operation: if we go too fast the milk will drip down the back of his throat and, as he's too weak to close off his larynx, the milk could go straight into his lungs – and that would be fatal. So we have to be patient.

Once he's had a feed Sara and I massage him, which helps his blood to circulate. He seems so small in my hands – it's hard to believe his thin, spindly legs, which are like twigs, could grow into the powerful limbs we see on adult kangaroos.

Then we wrap him up in his beanie and a few towels, trying to mimic the environment of his mother's pouch, and leave him to sleep on a counter, accompanied by a sign asking everyone to please not disturb him. After all, he's busy . . . resting!

I see other patients but check on Beanie intermittently and after six hours I'm pleasingly impressed by his progress. But the next twenty-four hours will really decide if he has a future. Without the comfort and warmth of his mother's pouch, and without her food, he's had to grow up before his time. It's up to him, and us, to see if he can survive such a trauma.

By the day's end I decide to take Beanie home with me. He will need three-hourly feeds through the night. His condition is still critical, but I'm hopeful – he is willing to eat and seems to be cheerfully taking whatever treatment we give him. If I can just keep him stable during the night with warmth and food, I predict Beanie will be with us for a while yet.

The car trip home is probably a bit unusual for Beanie – so I've put the heater on to try to minimise the discomfort; but then again, he's been through so much trauma in the past few days that maybe it's nothing compared to all that. Once we're through the door I turn on the electric blanket in my bed. Then I massage lanolin – which is a by-product of sheep's wool – into his skin to moisturise it and insulate him from the cold.

I give him a feed, which is becoming less of a struggle each time, as I've finally found the perfect drinking position for him. He likes being upright and if I squeeze his head back a little bit, he starts drinking quite enthusiastically.

Once he's tucked up again in his beanie and towels, he goes into my bed with the electric blanket.

I set my alarm for the first night's feed, three hours from now. I know from past experience that, even though I'm meant to be getting up every three to four hours, it's not like that. I don't get up, feed the animal, go back to bed then get up again three hours later. I'll get up and, with fingers crossed, go and check that he's still alive, feed him and go back to bed – but I don't sleep. There's always a constant nagging doubt and worry the whole way through the night that the animal I am caring for is not going to make it, so there is no way I can close my eyes and relax. I know tonight will be no different.

19

Billy and His Golf Balls

Over the years I have observed that lots of dogs and cats like to collect things or perform repetitive tasks – small, obsessive routines that they never seem to shake no matter how long they live. Cats are probably more likely to be the collectors – they bring things back to their owners as a sign of respect. Sometimes it's mice or snakes; sometimes it's kitchen scourers. Dogs usually tend towards the repetitive task end of the spectrum – they chase things. Over and over and over. For hours, if their owner is willing to indulge them.

So it is with Billy, a seven-month-old Jack Russell cross who just can't get enough of a golf ball. His owner, Adam, throws it and Billy retrieves it, and he never seems to tire of the routine; according to Adam, Billy could chase the ball for an hour or so, even if he doesn't always bring it back. The problem is that his body has become tired. As

Adam explains, 'He was playing in a park with a dog and got bowled over, and had a limp after that. And the limp just hasn't improved.'

Adam brings Billy to the clinic concerned that his little mate isn't really using his left hind leg. He clearly dotes on Billy, and Billy loves him right back. In fact, if Adam wasn't taking so much care of his dog, he probably wouldn't have even noticed Billy's problem.

'I wouldn't mind getting Billy in the corridor out there,' I say to Adam, 'and see him actually chase this ball. I want to see how that leg performs and then I want to see if he actually limps as a result of that, because the thrill of the chase often overrides any pain. If he's still limping through it then it's a pretty serious injury he's got there.'

Sure enough, Billy's limp is noticeable even when he's in hot pursuit of his beloved golf ball. I explain to Adam my concern and let him know that we will need to X-ray Billy's leg to find out what is causing the limp. As soon as I examine the film I can see the problem. The cartilage and bone around Billy's hip joint – the head of the femur or thigh bone – has been almost completely destroyed. Small dogs can be hyperactive, so they're prone to going too hard with their exercise, and while Billy is young his small size can't support his overly active lifestyle. In addition, there are very small blood vessels around the hip; through the inflammation and the swelling of the injury, the blood vessel that supplies blood to the top of the femur has been unable to get the blood through, and as a result the bone has essentially died. Billy is going to need to have the head of his femur removed.

This is a major operation for a small dog – quite traumatic for his body. As hard as it sounds I'll need to chip away at the bone to remove it.

I break the news to Adam as gently as I can without pulling any punches: 'I know he's young and I know he's managing okay but what I'm recommending is something fairly drastic.'

'Surgery?' Adam says, looking slightly incredulous.

'Yep. So what we need to do is go in there and remove this bone.'

'And what happens then?'

'He can actually function without the hip joint. He'll still walk on four legs. He'll actually walk better than he is now. I'm not going to lie to you – what I'm proposing here is a big operation, it's a decent operation. It's going to hurt, but unfortunately we don't really have another option.'

'If it has to be done it has to be done,' Adam says. 'I can't leave him in pain like this.'

I quite often see owners who are overcome when their pets are sick or are in need of surgery. I need to help them get over the emotional strain of it and work through to the realisation of what they have to do. It's too easy to project human feelings onto an animal – after all, the pet doesn't know it's about to have an operation; Billy won't know that when he comes out of the operation he's missing his hip joint. The hard part for Adam will be not to put too many of his own values onto Billy when Billy can't really understand – and doesn't need to know – exactly what's going on. The worrying is really for us. Not that we'd show it!

I believe Billy's youth will help him recover quickly, and he can live a normal life without a functioning hip joint on that one leg. Because he's small he doesn't have a lot of body weight, so each leg doesn't need to provide a lot of support. There are enough muscles and fibrous connective tissue in that affected leg for him to walk. If it is left untreated the pain will increase and it is a certainty that Billy's movement will eventually be severely constricted with arthritis.

I don't often see that kind of injury in a little dog; it's usually a case of the bigger the dog, the more likely they are to get hip problems. In big dogs there is more weight going through their hips and therefore more force meaning it's more likely that movement will damage it. But owners beware: if your dog chases tennis balls or sticks for more than twenty minutes a day, it's a very real risk that it will have no hip joint left by the age of five. Leash walking may seem a bit boring, but it means that the dog walks in a very controlled way, which doesn't put extra unnecessary strain on its joints (and you get some exercise as well).

The trick with Billy will be limiting his return to his golf ball routine – and that will be harder than his recovery from the operation, because his love of the golf ball is really an obsession. Small dogs like Billy, especially, are aware that they're little dogs in a big person's world. If they can have a possession or a talent that makes them feel more important and more of a contributor to the family unit, then they will embrace it wholeheartedly. Billy feels as though he impresses Adam each time he chases that ball. For him, it's the way they connect. If he was told to stop chasing the ball, it'd be like telling him, 'Sorry, you can no longer play with Adam!'

Billy will eventually find something else to take the place of the golf ball, but for his sake I hope it's a more passive pursuit.

On the day of Billy's operation, both he and Adam wait nervously in the waiting room.

'I didn't sleep very well last night, and I don't think Billy did either,' says Adam. 'He's getting very affectionate at the moment. I think he now senses that there's something about to happen as well.' Adam sighs. 'It's not easy.'

I am not surprised to hear what Adam is saying. Our animals do pick up on our moods and anxieties, recognise a change in routine and can sense when we are acting strangely.

We take Billy through and set him up in the operating room. I'm joined by Tony Mosman, the clinic's best orthopaedic surgeon. Tony has seen plenty of these types of injury before and we will operate together.

Billy's hip joint is covered by a decent layer of muscle so there's a fair amount of cutting to be done. I will then have to use a chisel-like tool to chip away at the head of Billy's femur. It takes a few taps, which does seem rather extreme in such a small dog, to get the job done and to break it off. Once we lay it on the table we can see the extent of the damage – the bone was just days away from collapsing. The fact is without this surgery, Billy could have been permanently disabled. He is lucky that Adam was paying attention and chose to act when he did.

The operation over, we bundle Billy off to recover. I am very pleased with how things went and just eighteen hours after surgery he is putting weight on his leg, which is above and beyond where we thought he'd be. I tell Adam that the prognosis is good.

20

Broken Heart

When my alarm goes off I realise with a shock that this is what it must be like having a newborn baby in the house – disrupting your own sleep for the good of an infant is something every parent does. I don't mind the fact that my deepest sleep was suddenly interrupted – I just want Beanie the joey to get better, even if it means a few 'vague' days ahead!

Earlier that night I'd found that my new housemate liked to feed propped up with his head tilted back, rather than in a lying position. So after I wake him up I make sure he's vertical and fix the bottle into place. He eats greedily, and I'm encouraged at the sight. The more he eats the more energy he'll have, and that means he's one more step away from danger.

After he's finished eating I tuck him back into bed, but there's no real prospect of me going back to sleep. I sit on the couch in a bit of a daze and doze. Somehow, three more hours pass.

I'd like to say that I'm always cool and calm around the animals I treat, and their owners. That I never become emotional. That I'm like a lot of human doctors: I can give the bad news without getting upset, and I can see an animal in distress and not take it on board. But I can't say that, because it's just not true. No matter what I may show on the outside, each animal has an impact on me. I wouldn't be in this job otherwise. I became a vet because I wanted to help animals, and if I feel that I've failed to do that, it's devastating.

It's even harder to take when it's an animal who is close to my heart, and the animals I take home are usually just that. They're the animals who need special attention, who I want to watch over a bit more closely. I think Beanie is the one who's meant the most to me recently, because he is so vulnerable and so in need of help – and also because he's not a cat or a dog: this is a little *kangaroo*, alone in the big city. He's a native animal who's been left an orphan, and struggling for his life, because humans have encroached on his natural habitat. He is symbolic of everything that can go wrong for our wildlife. We want them around because they're part of our national identity, but their proximity to human settlement does sometimes cause a few issues.

So I feel a great degree of responsibility as I go to wake Beanie for his next feed. I lift him out of the bed, where the electric blanket is still firing, and unwrap the towels. I rub his little paws and call to him. But there's nothing. No movement. No noise. Only three hours ago he was feeding well; surely he must just be asleep, so I move him around a bit more. There's nothing.

He's dead.

I can't really describe what I feel in the flash of knowing that he's gone. It is too strong to say it's like losing a member of your family, but it's close. And the emotional shock is only amplified by the numbing quiet of the house at this time of the morning. Mostly, I feel like I have let him down and in my head I run over all the different ways that might have happened. Did I feed him too much? Too little? Maybe he was too hot – or too cold? Should I have left him at the clinic? Perhaps bringing him home was too much – too many different environments in too short a space of time.

Nothing changes the fact, though: Beanie is not breathing, and never will again. I put my head in my hands.

When Beanie first came in to the clinic he looked for all the world like he wasn't going to make it, and we beat that. Last night I watched him drinking well and sitting up; I was sure he was going to pull through.

I spend the rest of the night mulling over everything I've done and trying to work out where I went wrong, even though I realise I'll never really know. It's possible that Beanie had just had too much trauma and been malnourished for too long, and no matter what I did he would have died. I don't like to accept that idea – I always believe we can do more – but thinking about it isn't going to help him now. It's the frustrating reality of caring for wildlife. They are incredibly fragile. You never feel totally confident they will pull through.

As I walk into the clinic that morning I have to break the news to the nurses. I know they'll be as upset as I am. But Sara is pragmatic: 'You can't beat yourself up about it. Hindsight's a fine thing. We can only do what we did. We put him on heat, we fed him, we gave him lots of love as well and that's just as important for these young animals. You can only do the best you can. Some you win, some you lose, and we've found that a lot with wildlife. If you make it, it's great; if you don't, that's when we cry.'

But if we didn't get upset, that would be worse: to become immune to the little tragedies of animal life, to care so little about our wildlife that we'd turn them away, would mean we should give up our jobs because we have lost the very sense of duty and care that took us into vet work in the first place.

No: as tough as it can be, I wouldn't give up this heartache. It keeps me anchored in the duties I need to perform and tied to the animals who need help. But I wish it had been different.

21

Attack of the Killer Chihuahua

I think you would have realised by now that I like all types of animals. Sure, I have my favourites and my not-so-favourites, but I don't dislike any animal. Sometimes, though, I have to work *really, really* hard to maintain that position . . .

This particular morning I check the computer for my appointments and see a name . . . The name of a once-a-year visitor who makes me instantly want to have a stiff drink at nine in the morning.

Bella.

Cute name, isn't it? Makes you think of a sweet little Cavalier King Charles or maybe a pampered Bondi poodle. But let me assure you that the most vicious and potentially deadly creature around Bondi isn't a shark lurking in the shadows behind a sandbar. It's a chihuahua. This Bella is a long-haired chihuahua and to the average punter she probably seems tiny and cute and fluffy. The truth is that she's my nemesis; my pint-sized, take-no-prisoners sworn enemy. She despises everything I stand for. But despite this and despite trying not to I can't help but find her fascinating. Almost like some bizarre form of Stockholm Syndrome I keep loving back. It's something I may regret. She's my least-trusted patient because she is, to be completely honest, an absolute terror.

Once a year Bella's owners, Tonya and Jamie, bring her in for a worming tablet and her vaccination. I suspect that over the course of the last few years Bella has learned to recognise me as 'the man with the needle' and this is part of the reason she makes the decision to get in first. There's also the fact that I desexed her. *Maybe* that has something to do with it as well . . . But, seriously, I'm the one who should be afraid – and I'll let the facts speak for themselves.

Since I started training as a vet I've had five dog bites. One was from a Rottweiler who needed its nails clipped. As I clipped the first one the owner said, 'Oh yeah, he doesn't like his nails being clipped.' As though punctuating his owner's statement, the Rottweiler sunk his teeth onto the back of my head. Three of them have been from corgis. I'll let you in on a little secret: corgis can be man-haters. Almost never woman-haters – just man-haters. And I've felt the brunt of many of them.

Then there's Bella. Bella counts as my last dog bite, but in truth she's bitten me so many times that in an almost desperate attempt to play down the monstering I get from a one kilogram Titan I just count her as one.

So perhaps now you can understand my desire for a drink when I see her name in the appointment list for the day. And I can assure you my heart beats a little faster as she comes into the room . . . and it isn't from love.

Sometimes people are surprised that I haven't had more dog bites, but I'd say a lot of vets have the same scorecard. We get very good at picking which animals are going to have a go and which ones aren't – it's all to do with their body language. If we're in doubt about a dog's propensity to bite, we put a muzzle on them.

I chatted to Lisa one day about reading animals' behaviour and body language. 'I think when you work with animals so closely,' she says, 'and you see them when they're healthy and when they're sick, you're in much more intense situations dealing with them so you're more able to recognise when they're in pain and stressed. The owners – and more so people who don't know animals – wouldn't ever be in that kind of close and tense situation with them.

'We're taught animal behaviour and body language and things like that, but I think it's just the more you spend time with them the more you realise what they're feeling and how they're going to react. And there are owners out there who've had dogs all their lives and are very in touch with their animals, and they're pretty good at it as well.

'Some people just have that connection with animals and others don't, and maybe that's because people who love animals give off certain body language to the animals and the animals are receptive to that. And if people are scared of animals . . . it's often when you're nervous of dogs that you show them that you're nervous, then they can be more in your face. So maybe it's just how we trust them as well.'

I restrain myself from telling her that there's nothing on earth that could make me trust Bella. Instead, we talk about cats. I've had a lot of scratches – I get a scratch probably weekly – but the scratches are never as deep as a dog bite; they're more of a glancing thing. And you can hold cats by the scruff of the neck if they're misbehaving, which lessens the chances of being bitten. It doesn't hurt them – it just controls them. The scruff thing just doesn't work so well on a dog.

'I'm probably more nervous of cats than I am of dogs in terms of them being aggressive,' says Lisa, 'but I can judge it. There are cats that I will not pick up and cuddle because I walk up and open the cage and they're swiping at me as I open the cage. It's really just a matter of judgement which ones you think are genuinely being aggressive. Because there are different types of aggression – some are being aggressive because they're scared and they're in pain, and some are being aggressive because they're being dominant or territorial of their cage. If an animal's fearful you're going to pick them up and make them feel calm and talk to them nicely – you have to try to take away their fear. Whereas with one that's just being dominant or territorial there's not much you can do.'

When it is time to treat Bella, her owner Jamie attempts to hold her still while I try to jab her with a needle. It isn't going too well and Bella is snarling at me. For such a petite little thing she is incredibly menacing, but apparently I'm the only person she reacts to like this.

We face off against each other: I try to time my jab to get in before she whips her head around to attack me. I suspect that Jamie could do a better job holding her down . . . Maybe no man is capable of controlling this beast! Tonya obviously agrees with my suspicions and takes over. This time I'm able to get the needle in with a millisecond to spare before she can bite me.

Next: the worming tablet. This is an even less fun activity, as I have to place the tablet in Bella's mouth – right next to her long, sharp teeth. A tricky dance begins, consisting of me quickly moving my fingers towards her mouth and her quickly trying to remove those fingers with her teeth.

I eventually get the tablet in, but as always when it comes to Bella there's a price: she manages to sink one of her canines into my hand. Blood streams down my finger and I can just tell she'll be proud of that. She'll go home now and sit on the couch and think, 'Even though it's another year before I get to see him, he's going to feel it, he's going to know about it and he's going to be waiting anxiously for next year.'

So she's won – again. Thankfully not quite by knock-out, just a narrow points decision. In fact, the record will show that we both 'took' our medicine! But she doesn't know that next year I have a plan, I am going to quietly reschedule her with another vet in the clinic . . . someone new who won't realise that the name Bella should instil fear. Well, that's the idea I have come up with today anyway.

Health-care Tips for Your Puppy or Dog

Vaccination

You should have your puppy vaccinated against:

1. Canine Parvovirus – a viral gastroenteritis that is highly contagious.
2. Canine Distemper – a highly contagious disease producing signs such as fever, depression, loss of appetite and discharge of pus from the eyes and nose.
3. Canine Hepatitis – in puppies hepatitis may cause sudden death, and it is also very dangerous for adult dogs.
4. Canine Parainfluenza Virus and Bordetella (Canine Cough) – both highly contagious diseases, especially in enclosed places such as boarding kennels.

Your puppy will require several vaccinations at the following ages:

- 6–8 weeks – first vaccination
- 10–12 weeks – booster shot
- 14–16 weeks – final vaccination

Adult dogs require an annual vaccination booster for the rest of their life.

Heartworm Prevention

Heartworm is spread by mosquitoes and can prove lethal if it's allowed to develop untreated. Again, prevention is the best form of cure, as even treating them once they have it can be dangerous.

You should start giving your dog monthly preventative medication from the age of ten to twelve weeks. Once your dog is a year old it can have an annual injection instead. Your dog will need to be protected for the rest of its life.

Worming

Worms such as tapeworm and hookworm are a common cause of illness in dogs. Puppies should be wormed at two, four, six, eight, ten and twelve weeks of age, then every month until they are six months old and then every three months for the rest of their life. The worming treatment commonly takes the form of a tablet or other digestible medication.

Regular Check-ups

It's advisable for your dog to at least have yearly check-ups with a vet, just like you'd go to the dentist regularly. A regular check-up will help your vet detect or prevent health problems before they develop.

Dental Care

It's important to keep your cat's and dog's teeth and gums clean. This can be achieved by giving them something appropriate to chew on, such as a toy (check that it's pet safe – you don't want a toy that can break into pieces easily when chewed).

22

Roxie

We know a lot about humans giving birth, but not much of a fuss is made about animals and the birth process. Maybe we humans think it's more 'natural' for our pets than it is for us, and to a certain extent there's more practicality in animal births: the animals certainly don't stay in hospital for a few days, particularly if they're farm animals like the Clarks' cow – they have to get back to work or just simply get on with being animals. A sheep gives birth in a field standing up and, all being well, ewe and lamb trot off to join the flock not long after the lamb enters the world. The newborn has to be walking, eating and making noises almost immediately.

However, this doesn't mean that the birthing mother doesn't feel anything – that it's a seamless, pain-free process that can have a cow chewing cud while pushing out a calf. Things can go wrong, and they do – sometimes the mothers get birth paralysis and go down while they're in labour, which can mean the death of the young; other times the baby 'presents' the wrong way . . . or the birth may be premature, and there are the same kind of complications in an animal newborn that result from human premature births. And if you've ever seen the face of an animal in labour, you'll know that it's not an enjoyable experience.

Five-year-old Roxie, a beagle, is rushed to SASH in labour. Lisa Chimes is on this case. Sadly, Roxie's labour is not a cause for celebration – she has already delivered three dead puppies, and it is imperative that Lisa checks to see if there are any still in her uterus, dead or alive.

Roxie's distress is plain to see: she looks upset and she is agitated. She has arrived in a cardboard box, which is what she was sitting in when she gave birth to the first three pups, and she's extremely reluctant to leave it.

'We going to try to get you out of this box somehow,' Lisa says gently as Roxie whines, 'because I can't really look at you in there.'

No doubt, being aware that her first three puppies haven't survived, Roxie fears what will happen if she doesn't have the security of the box.

Although dogs can't tell us their emotions, they do feel the same sort of primitive concern for their young that we feel for ours. Roxie knows something is wrong. Luckily for Lisa and nurse Jess, she graciously accepts human help. A snarling pregnant dog would be another complication altogether.

Jess lifts Roxie out of the box so Lisa can check her out.

Above: It's not unusual for parrots to become besotted with their owners. This is Harry with his owner, Chrissie. Investigating why he was losing his feathers led to the discovery that Harry was obsessed … and not with crackers.

Right: You don't grow up as a vet's son among a menagerie of animals without picking up some party tricks. Hypnotising chooks or ducks is not difficult. Don't try this with a Doberman.

Little Paddy the fairy penguin was found much the worse for wear near Bondi Beach. After examining him I took him home to gauge his recovery. After a few days he was on the mend so I contacted Taronga Zoo, who looked after him while he recuperated. Two weeks later, he was well enough to be released back into the wild. He was set free in Sydney Harbour with another fairy penguin; the last I saw of Paddy he was swimming away. It was a great result.

Even though I am a vet in an urban environment I still get to practise on farm animals. This is Lady, one of the many animals living a bucolic life in the grounds of historic Vaucluse House in Sydney. I was called out to trim her hooves – what you could call a goat manicure. Any hoofed animals living in the city need to be monitored to make sure their hooves don't grow too long and hinder movement.

This little Eastern Grey kangaroo came into the clinic in a very bad way. His mother had been killed by a car and a family discovered him with her dead body. Everyone in the clinic fell in love with this little fellow – but the odds were sadly against him. I called him Beanie and crossed my fingers that I could make a difference.

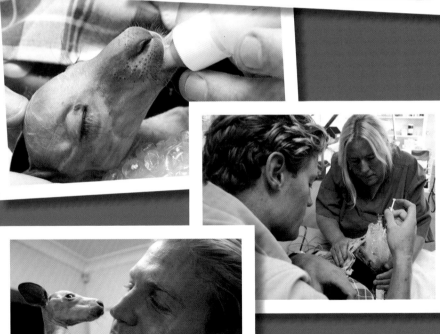

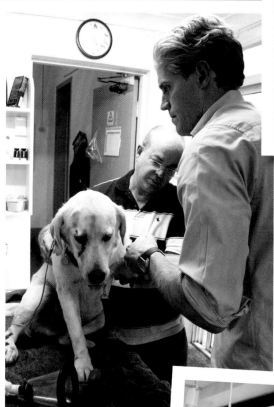

Above: Elroy's owners were worried about how he'd look after desexing. They chose testicular implants for him so no one would know his secret.

Above: Too often I have to deal with the aftermath of a meeting between an animal and a vehicle, and the animal always comes off second best. Cody the labrador is one of the lucky ones.

Right: Lisa Chimes is a vet at SASH – the Small Animal Specialist Hospital – in Sydney's northwest. Lisa is the perfect person to investigate the sudden illness affecting this young kitten called Felix.

Delivering the young of a large animal is extremely physical work and very, very messy. This calf was stuck so I had to work hard to help it shift. As soon as the newborn's on the ground I try to get all the mucus out of its mouth then annoy it a little bit, which stimulates its nerves so all its sensations come to life. This then triggers a breath – and that's what I'm waiting for. The mother doesn't take long to say hello.

Near the clinic there's a massive Westfield shopping centre. It's a sprawling complex housing department stores, restaurants and cinemas – and also a family of peregrine falcons who have been living at the top of the tower for years. These birds of prey are one type of animal I very rarely see up close. There's not much opportunity to treat them in the wild, and even less in the city. After a call from the security manager I ended up looking after two falcons, a breeding pair. After two days of care they were ready to be released back into the wild (*above*). Sadly, when I checked their nest I found out their chicks hadn't survived. While I was investigating I was swooped by another falcon, who didn't like me invading his territory. Just look at the determination on this bird's face (*below*).

Left: Great Danes are the gentle giants of the dog world. Although they can seem intimidating – they're the tallest breed of dog in the world – I find they are usually pretty placid around humans … thankfully!

Below: I can't imagine life without my own dog, Rusty. He's a kelpie who came from a farm adjacent to my parents' property near Stroud in New South Wales. He is a bit shy of strangers but he's my little mate and I wouldn't be without him.

'There's no puppy in the pelvic canal,' Lisa says after her first examination. 'Let's go get a pelvic X-ray of you, hon.'

Roxie is taken to the X-ray room and, no doubt confused, is lain out on the table while the film is taken. When she reviews the X-ray, Lisa can see that there are three more puppies. Given what has happened to the first three, it's unlikely that any of them are alive, but they can't stay in there – if Roxie doesn't give birth to them, they will rot inside her, she will get septicaemia and possibly die. A caesarean section is an option, but it's not the preferred one as it would mean that Roxie may not be able to have more pups later on. The best possible result for Roxie's long-term health is for her to give birth to these pups.

As Roxie's labour has stalled, Lisa gives her an injection of oxytocin to restart it; it's the same drug that is given to women to induce labour.

'A little pinch,' Lisa tells Roxie as she gives her the injection.

Now Lisa and Jess have to wait and keep comforting Roxie all the while.

23

Rosie and Angus

Back at the Bondi Clinic I have a visit from Rosie, a gorgeous golden retriever. She is a playful and sweet-natured dog (the complete antithesis of Bella), and she is absolutely devoted to her owner, Angus.

Angus found Rosie through an advertisement in the newspaper. She seemed almost too good to be true at only 100 dollars, as usually retrievers will sell for a lot more than that. It was a price Angus could afford but he soon found out why she didn't cost much: her two front paws were badly deformed. The previous owner told Angus that he hadn't been feeding her properly, so Angus thought the damage may have been caused by rickets. It wasn't enough to put him off.

'I think it was a case of love at first sight,' says Angus. 'She chose me and I chose her. In terms of Rosie's future, she certainly can't exercise as a normal dog, she can't get up stairs, and I just think those things are going to get worse.'

Angus is right. When he brings Rosie in to see us at Bondi I refer him to SASH, as Rosie is going to need specialist treatment for what I suspect is a serious developmental problem. If nothing is done, Rosie will end up with severe arthritis and sores on the parts of the legs she'd be using to walk on; a result of her scraping her skin on the ground.

'I'm determined to do what I can for her,' says Angus as he leaves the clinic.

Angus takes Rosie to SASH, where she's examined by Andrew Marchevsky, who is a specialist in small animal surgery with extensive experience in all aspects of surgery.

'Rosie's condition is serious in the sense that I think it's life-threatening if it goes on for much longer,' says Andrew. 'She won't be able to walk around; she'll be in chronic pain. And from an ethical point of view you just wouldn't be able to keep her alive.'

The situation is this: Rosie has an inherited bone disease and it has damaged her growth plates, distorting the bones in her forelegs. Andrew says it's an extreme case – he believes that even within another month Rosie wouldn't have much of a life. The treatment he suggests is extensive – he will need to break her legs, pin them and put them in frames so they can be gradually straightened out. It's an expensive treatment. The bill will run to over 6000 dollars, because there are two affected legs.

'I think your hundred-dollar dog is going to turn into something more than that,' he tells Angus. It is a very hard decision for Angus to make.

Says Lisa, who meets Rosie when she comes to SASH, 'Long term it wouldn't be fair on the dog to leave her like that, particularly with both limbs deformed. It would affect her quality of life – she wouldn't be able to run around normally.'

In order to afford the operation, Angus says, 'I'm going to have to talk to family and friends. I'm going to have to go into debt. It's a lifetime commitment, taking on an animal, and it's something that I feel I have to take some responsibility for.'

Andrew decides that he will go ahead with the treatment. His emotional attachment to Rosie won't let him walk away from her even though he never imagined having to make such a big financial outlay. He takes his responsibilities as a pet owner very seriously and so commits to what is necessary to give Rosie a chance at a long, happy and functioning life.

Rosie's operation is almost as big a procedure as it gets for a dog, taking three and a half hours, and the recovery will be very slow. As Andrew says, 'If you were a human you'd be in hospital for weeks after this. It's very major surgery, especially for a young dog.'

It's lucky for Rosie that Angus is so dedicated to her as he'll need to tighten the screws on her braces to help the bones knit back together in the right way. Rosie's frames need to be adjusted every day for the next three weeks. It will then take the fractured legs another six weeks to heal.

'It's a long journey for Rosie and Angus,' says Andrew. 'I think Rosie will probably cope with it better than Angus will. But we'll see.'

When Angus arrives he admits that he's 'a bit spun out, to be honest with you. God, she's been through a lot.' He is distressed to see the reality of Rosie's operation. 'You're handling this better than me, darling,' he tells her as her tail bravely thumps the floor. 'You're a good girl, Rosie.'

'She's a great little patient,' says Andrew. 'She has a great temperament. She's a good candidate for this sort of surgery because she is so accepting.'

Other dogs who have procedures like this have the option of physiotherapy and hydrotherapy baths. An animal physiotherapist visits SASH every few weeks to do physical therapy on the animals. Says Lisa, 'They're mammals and we're mammals, and it benefits us so there's no reason it's not going to benefit them.'

However, Rosie is probably a bit different to the dogs who usually have such therapies. We don't often see dogs like Rosie out and about, as Lisa explains: 'Seeing those limb deformities is not that common because those dogs don't ever get sold.' There are, of course, lots of dogs that are bred for shows and to look a certain way. Unfortunately, pure breeding can result in genetic deformities such as Rosie's. Says Lisa, 'Hopefully because of the way the breed standards are improving and we've got those crossbreeds out there, it won't necessarily occur often.'

*   *   *

After the harrowing operation Andrew is pleased enough with Rosie's progress and Angus takes her home to begin her healing. Angus's other dog, Gus, keeps a constant vigil by Rosie's bedside and Angus steels himself to tighten Rosie's screws each day.

'As each day goes by I'm seeing a little bit of improvement,' he says when we catch up with him a week or so later. 'I don't think she's in a lot of pain, so that's been a real relief for me too.'

Lisa reports that Rosie is bearing up under the strain of the changes to her legs: 'She's doing really well – her legs are almost straight. It doesn't even faze her, having all the adjustments made. She's happy and wags her tail and owns the place.' And despite the financial cost, Angus doesn't regret for a moment that Rosie is the dog he chose to bring into his life.

I am pleased that this situation has worked out for Angus and Rosie, but it does help underline the importance of carefully weighing up all the issues when you are considering taking on a pet. I can't stress this enough . . . a pet is for life and so you have to be sure this is what you want and not a fleeting fad. Be careful about your choice of pet and seek out as much information as you can about the animal you are thinking of buying or adopting. I am sure many vet clinics would be happy to help you with advice.

What Should You Ask a Breeder When You're Choosing a Dog?

- Ask to meet the parents of the animal to make sure the temperament and type fits what you are seeking.
- Ask about inherited problems with the breed and any testing that should be done to diagnose these.
- Ask about any pre-existing medical conditions.
- Request contact details from the breeder to ensure you can get in touch with any questions or concerns after receiving your dog.

Source: Dog Breeders Australia – www.dogbreeders.net.au

24

No
Hope

Back at SASH, the oxytocin has taken effect and Roxie is
starting to have contractions. The decision is made to
put her back in her cardboard box – she was so attached to
it, it makes sense to let her use it for this trying time – and
she is being watched over by nurse Jess. Like most vet nurses
and vets, Jess takes a pet's suffering to heart and she is almost
as distressed as Roxie. She can only guess at what Roxie must
be thinking and feeling, but it's probably not good. Because
her first three pups were stillborn there is a better-than-
average chance that the three remaining puppies will also be
born dead. It is a heartbreaking scenario for any mother,
human or not, and for anyone who is there to witness it.

Suddenly there's a shift in Roxie's demeanour.

'We have a puppy,' Jess announces.

'Excellent,' Lisa replies as she arrives at Roxie's side. 'Good
girl, Rox.'

And there it is – tiny, not moving, not even really looking like a puppy. It has probably been dead inside Roxie for a while, although she instinctively tries to nuzzle it.

'It's very small, isn't it,' Lisa says, looking upset. 'It's very underdeveloped.'

'There's another one,' Jess says almost immediately, as she struggles to control her emotions. 'There is no way there is anything living in this dog.' Jess leans down to cuddle Roxie.

'It's got to be pretty tough for her,' says Lisa. 'She has to go through the whole birthing process and then she doesn't have the pups in the end.'

Roxie is panting, possibly still in labour. Lisa and Jess both know there's another puppy left inside their patient – and it has to come out.

25

Puppy School

The veterinary clinic where I work is primarily a place for treating animals who are sick or in need of a check-up. But one night a week it serves as a meeting place for a semi-secret group of Bondi residents who gather together for mutual support and guidance, some tough love, and the odd bit of tennis-ball-throwing.

You may know it as 'puppy school'.

One of the clinic nurses, Sara Ashdown, runs one of the groups, which takes place after hours so people can make it there at the end of the working day. It's always full of a diverse mob of dogs and their owners, but they all have one thing in common: they have puppies who need to be trained.

'I get really happy going to puppy school,' says Sara. 'It's like a buzz. People get puppies with the intention that they're like little stuffed toys. They're not, because there's poo coming out, they're barking and chewing. It's like bringing a baby into your household and we get people at their wits' end saying, "Help me". Some of the puppies are really good but I tend to get the naughty ones in my class.'

I'm of the firm belief that all owners should take their pets to obedience school. If dogs don't have a grounding in what is the right or correct behaviour then, really, they're never taught right from wrong – and what hope would their owners ever have of controlling them? Puppy school is the most basic training that a dog should have, it gives them the language that forms the foundation for everything else.

If you can get your dog to sit or stay or drop, you have their attention forever. If a dog that's absolutely out of control can be made to sit, then you immediately have its attention over any other thing that's going on around them. And every single behaviourial technique, every single training or bit of control over a dog relies on the dog being focused on their owner and on their owner having their pet's attention.

Aside from revision sessions, puppy school usually takes an hour a week for four weeks – which is really not much. I'm not too impressed with owners who can't be bothered allocating that time when it's not an onerous amount and it's such an important thing to do. The pets will not feel forced to be there – that is a human emotion. Pets love to learn and love to impress their owners when they are given the tools to do so. To deprive them of that opportunity and set them – and you – up for a lifetime of misbehaviour is beyond foolish.

Puppy school isn't just for puppies, either, because – despite rumours to the contrary – you *can* teach an old dog new tricks. It's a bit slower and harder than with a pup, but it's possible. You often need to redefine their habits. So it's doable, but the younger the better, really – like humans, dogs learn better when they're young.

Sara has just the right personality for running the puppy school. She adores all kinds of animals, and she has a friendly but firm hand on all the puppies who attend – and their owners.

Some of the puppies are in dire need of the school – like Yogi, whose owner, Kirsty, says, 'It's very full-on, constantly retrieving my dog from attacking other dogs.' If you can call being jumped by a one kilogram puppy an attack!

Then there's Harvey. His owner, Maureen, says, 'Harvey gets up to pretty much everything he's not supposed to. His favourite thing at the moment is chewing just the left leg of my jeans. I was considering buying a new sofa – but that's on hold because he's ripped the other one to shreds. He won't sleep in his own bed. He just gives you those little eyes and you think, "Oh, it's okay, you don't need to learn that".'

As if to prove the point, Harvey poos in the clinic's hallway. But later, as the pups are put through their paces and expected to respond to commands, Harvey performs better than the others. It's a good sign for Maureen.

One possibly unexpected outcome for the puppy school attendees is that the puppies' owners find that they bond with the other animals – and with each other. Friendships are formed and puppies are tamed. Sounds like the perfect kind of school.

26

Bittersweet

Lisa has to give Roxie another oxytocin injection in the hope of stimulating her uterus to contract and release the last puppy.

'Little stings,' she tells the beagle as the needle goes in, while Jess strokes Roxie's head. 'It's been a hard day today for you,' Lisa says as she rubs the injection site.

After another bout of contractions, the final puppy is born. Lisa is resigned as she picks it up – it is even smaller than the two delivered before it. Lisa tells Roxie that she is going to take away her last puppy and tries to comfort the distressed dog. The mothering instinct is strong, regardless of whether the puppy can respond or not. But it's been upsetting for the staff at SASH to witness Roxie's tragedy.

'There's nothing worse than delivering a whole litter full of dead puppies,' says Lisa. 'We just really have to look at it from the positive point of view – that Roxie's okay.'

Now that her ordeal is over, Roxie makes a quick recovery – another testament to the incredible fortitude of animals. As soon as her owners, Jason and Amanda, arrive, she jumps up and wags her tail. It's a positive sign on what has been a very bleak day for this little braveheart.

Then Lisa sets the record straight: 'Roxie may look okay but she's under a lot of stress. Humans go through a huge ordeal when they deliver a baby and animals do too.'

'We're sad that the pups didn't turn out,' says Jason, 'but she's a lovely dog and a lovely companion, and we're just happy that she's still here. It's bittersweet, really.'

Dogs and Pregnancy

How will you know if your dog is pregnant?

A vet can usually detect pregnancy between weeks four and six by feeling the dog's abdomen. Pregnancy can also be detected by an ultrasound scan and X-ray.

Your dog's weight may increase and you should notice that her abdomen is growing in size, and her mammary glands are growing larger and more red. She may also produce milk.

How long does a dog's pregnancy last?

The canine gestation period is fifty-eight to sixty-three days. If the pregnancy lasts longer than sixty-four days you should inform your vet.

What should dogs eat while they're pregnant?

If your pregnant dog is eating a well-balanced diet there is no need to supplement it with extra calcium or vitamins – it may, in fact, be dangerous to do this.

Further into the pregnancy the pups will occupy more and more space in the mother's abdomen – just as with humans – and while your dog may need to eat a lot more, she'll have to eat smaller meals more frequently.

How do you tell if your dog is in labour?

Approximately twenty-four hours before labour commences your dog may seem restless and off her food, and she'll begin to make a 'nest'. She may also start panting.

Once the abdominal contractions start, your dog will make heaving motions. The first puppy should be born within one to two hours of the first contractions. Just as with humans, the dog's waters may break before the first pup is born but it's not always the case – some pups are born completely covered in their placental membranes.

Do you need to cut the umbilical cord?

Your dog will usually sever the umbilical cord herself and remove the membranes from her pups. However, if she seems unable to do so, you can gently remove the membrane from the pup's nose and mouth. The pup should immediately take a breath, move around and attempt to suckle its mother.

How long will the birth take?

The mother usually rests between pups, anywhere from fifteen minutes to an hour. After the last puppy is born the dog's breathing will become noticeably calmer and she should be given some peace and quiet to be with her pups.

What are the possible complications?

Approximately forty per cent of pups are born tail first (we call it breech birth in humans) and this is normal. But if any of the following occur, call your vet:

• A puppy has not been born within one to two hours of contractions starting.

- Half an hour has gone by after the birth of a pup and your dog is still having strong contractions but another pup has not been born.
- A pup becomes stuck halfway. You can apply gentle pressure to the pup without a vet's assistance, but if it does not move easily then immediately call your vet.

Source: www.vetwest.com.au/pregnancy-and-your-dog

27

Charlie

I've already told you my belief that house calls can play an important role in managing the health of an animal – not only do they give vets more time to examine animals, but the animals and their owners tend to be more relaxed than they would be at the clinic. But even though I believe they are helpful I don't make that many house calls, with the exception of emergencies, mainly because to do them properly takes time. And there's just not enough of that in your average day at the clinic! I make even less regular house calls to the same house. But I always make an exception for Mrs Causewell.

Mrs Causewell, who is eighty-eight years old, is something of a Bondi institution – she has lived in the suburb for an untold number of years. She has two dogs, Mr Bojangles and Charlie. Make that two *living* dogs. Because she also has Mickey. Mickey was alive once. Now he's something of an exhibit in Mrs Causewell's living room. After he died she sent him to a taxidermist who, as it turned out, was the resident taxidermist at a major Sydney museum, so instead of Mickey returning looking like the loving family pet – perhaps curled up on a lazy Sunday night – he was returned to her looking quite a bit more ferocious than he had in life. I suspect the taxidermist thought he was stuffing a hyena or perhaps a sabre-tooth tiger, given the way the claws lunged forward, the eyes blazed wide with rage and the teeth were bared as if any visitor might be a meal.

I've come across a few people who have had a pet stuffed. It's an interesting way of remembering them, although I personally think photos work just as well and are a lot more portable. But each to their own. Some people like to remember their pets in a more physical way; sometimes it works for people who have difficulty coming to grips with the fact that their pet has gone. And if that helps you get through the day then who am I to make any judgement at all?

My biggest concern about having a pet stuffed is that I don't really know what the owner would do once they'd decided they'd moved through the grieving process and it was now time to say goodbye. You can't exactly put the animal out with the recyclables. It's a strange situation to be in. As Mrs Causewell said, 'There are some people I wouldn't want to see in my lounge room every day. Some people I would.' Mickey is obviously someone she wants to see in her lounge room every day.

Clearly, it's too late for me to do anything about Mickey. So the reason for my regular visits to Mrs Causewell is

Charlie, a nine-year-old Cavalier King Charles spaniel. Like a lot of small dogs, he has a congenital heart problem. Cavaliers are now a very popular breed – they have sweet temperaments and they like to hang around the house, so they make good companion dogs.

On this day I go to Mrs Causewell's house with Neil Coy, one of the clinic's nurses, so we can take Charlie back to the clinic for his weekly treatment and I can check his medications with Mrs Causewell.

Neil and the other clinic staff often run errands for Mrs Causewell; they also made up a chart for her so she can follow up on all the medication that Charlie needs.

'She's an amazing lady,' says Neil. 'She really takes great care of those pets. It's a bit worrying for me sometimes, I suppose, because I worry whether she's taking care of herself.'

So whenever I go to Mrs Causewell's house I always like to check in on her as well as her pets. She lives alone, and she's getting on a bit – the dogs may keep her company but they can't make her dinner. She seems in good spirits and healthy, so I can set my mind at ease on that score. Now we just need to attend to Charlie.

In the past Charlie and Mrs Causewell have battled for dominance in the household. Looking at the proud way he carries himself, I tell her King Charles looks very regal indeed!

'Oh yes,' she responds, 'he was a very bossy little bastard to start off with. But the older he got, the more he needed affection and realised that he needed to depend on me.'

Charlie's condition means that fluid builds up in his abdomen as his heart is not strong enough to pump all his blood around his body properly. Basically he has a leaking valve, so each time his heart pumps blood, some leaks back through that valve. As a result he gets a build-up of fluid in his circulation. This fluid then pools in his abdomen, causing him to look bloated. All that swelling also pushes on his lungs, making him breathless. It's not a painful condition – it's more an annoyance that lessens his quality of life. The unfortunate thing about heart disease is that there is no cure. We can manage it but we can't fix it. So it's just a matter of making your little patient as comfortable as you possibly can and convincing people that he doesn't look that way because of a few too many pies.

Once we have him back in the clinic, Neil cushions Charlie's head as I give the little dog an ultrasound to check his heart signs and to determine how much fluid is moving around inside him. He has a very big heart for such a small dog – it's like a balloon sitting in his chest, almost eight centimetres in diameter. It should be almost half that size, and because it's so big it pushes onto his lungs, making it even harder for him to breathe.

'His heart's doing its best to keep up,' I tell Neil, 'but unfortunately it just can't get the job done.' And really every millilitre of blood it can't pump is another millilitre that ends up in his abdomen, making his belly swell in size.

The fluid is Charlie's biggest clinical sign and his biggest aggravation, and that's where we *can* manage his condition – hence his fortnightly visits. And in terms of a treatment it's not that invasive – we may be putting a needle into him but it is not dissimilar to giving a vaccination. Only here we're taking something out rather than putting something in. Seen in that light, it's a pretty simple treatment for Charlie – five minutes every two weeks – to keep him going. And although his condition will one day kill him, I think a lot of owners would follow Mrs Causewell's lead and choose the constant treatment when the alternative is putting down their dog.

On this day we suck almost two litres of fluid out of Charlie using a motorised suction pump. Even though he only weighs eight kilograms, each visit we consistently drain between one and two litres of fluid. I find it amazing that he has the energy to produce that much fluid, let alone keep on living. He really is a tough little guy.

'It's hard watching him deteriorate,' Neil says. 'He's such a lovely dog, he has lots of personality – it makes me sad just thinking about it.'

After the treatment we return Charlie to Mrs Causewell and Mr Bojangles. They both seem pleased to have him home, and I can leave safe in the knowledge we'll be checking up on all of them again very soon.

28

Watch Out for that Snake!

Okay, so it is a sweeping generalisation but in my mind most dogs are very inquisitive animals and given half a chance love nothing more than poking around in gardens and bushland. This is when they can pick up ticks, which can become life-threatening, but sometimes their adventures can lead them into the path of something even more serious.

Seven-year-old Zoe, a Bichon Frisé, arrives at SASH suffering from a snakebite. Her attacker was a red-bellied black snake, and the SASH staff know this because her owner, Rick, found the snake dead in the garden, near where he found Zoe writhing in pain.

The red-bellied black snake is extremely venomous and Zoe needs to be treated swiftly if she's to survive. Dr Darren Foster is doing his best to insert a cannula so he can administer antiserum to Zoe, but she is resisting. As nurse Jess holds her and tries to keep her still, Zoe is squirming vigorously and making it impossible for Darren to inject her. It's no surprise she's wary – being bitten by a snake would make anyone suspicious of needles – but time is the critical factor here. The longer Zoe goes without the antiserum, the more likely it is that she will die of the snakebite. She has already been taken to two different vets before she arrived at SASH, so she's undoubtedly agitated because of that, too. Neither vet was equipped to deal with the serious situation that Zoe has found herself in, but luckily the second vet referred her to SASH.

Snakebite is one of the most serious dangers that can face Australian pets – especially inquisitive dogs and dog breeds known for their hunting instincts. The most dangerous time for a dog to be bitten is at the beginning of the snake season, when the weather is just starting to get warm, because, as SASH's Dr Lisa Chimes says, 'the snakes have had their venom sitting there while they've been in hibernation for so long and it's usually that first animal that they bite in which they inject the most amount of venom. Even in springtime the snakes start coming out because they need to bask in the sun to regulate their body temperature.

'But summer definitely has the highest incidence of snake bites,' Lisa explains. 'If the owners don't know the signs and the animal receives a lethal dose of venom, then the bite can be fatal. There are also delayed effects of snakebite. The dog will be bitten and they'll collapse and then can apparently recover, and twenty-four hours later they're ill again.

'Where I was working in Melbourne, because there are rivers right there, even in the city there are snakes. I didn't know that because I came from Sydney's Eastern Suburbs and we'd never see a snake in our garden. It was quite a shock to me to find when I started working in Melbourne that we were getting so many snakebites on animals. I saw many more than I do here in Sydney.'

So Zoe is one of the rare Sydney victims of snakebite, but she is in just the same amount of peril as a dog anywhere else. And the longer she evades Darren's cannula, the longer the venom has a chance to do irreparable damage.

29

The Owl, the Turtle and the Ferret

Though dogs and cats are probably my most typical patients I am never surprised to see any animal come through the door of the clinic. So when Barry from WIRES turns up with a boobook owl, it's interesting but not outstanding.

Boobooks are the smallest and most common owl found in Australia and they are also known as a mopoke by many people. If you have heard their distinctive call you know why. It sounds like they are saying mo-poke. They are fascinating birds and are nocturnal hunters so unless you are looking up at the trees at night you probably won't be lucky enough to come across one. Barry has brought this one in because it is showing signs of illness. I start my examination with the basics and there is no obvious signs of trauma or evidence of fractures in his wings. It's clear to me, though, that he hasn't eaten for quite a while, he seems too weak to catch his own food, and he's also very stressed, so any nutrition we can get into him is going to be very welcome.

We give him some food by mouth and he eats it enthusiastically. It is a very good sign. I also give him fluids subcutaneously, underneath his very fragile skin. A procedure that requires extreme care.

Neil is holding the bird for me while I inject him, and he looks at the owl with wonder: 'Perfectly designed, isn't he?' he says.

I talk to Barry and because there seems no reason for the boobook's signs of illness we decide to do some more tests and then Barry will continue to care for him and try to build him up so he can be released. It is the best scenario and I know he is in good hands with Barry and WIRES.

After I've taken care of the boobook's food and fluid, I realise that it has brought some fellow travellers: parasites that decide to jump to the nearest warm body – namely, me. Even though I slap them away, there's no way to be sure whether I've killed them all. The bugs are called hippoboscid flies aka feather lice . . . actually blood-sucking flies. I guess if I wake up scratching tonight, I'll know the cause.

Nurse Mel arrives at the clinic brandishing a container which is the temporary home to a turtle she's found. The turtle seemed to be a bit disoriented so, naturally enough, she's brought it to work to have it checked out and is now showing it to Tonya, who's just as curious about the creature as Mel

– but not half as curious as the turtle is about his new surroundings. It starts clambering over the desk and phones. He seems quite erratic and it's like he's carrying some kind of homing device that has its coordinates scrambled – north is east and south is west, or something like that.

Mel puts him back in his box and asks me to give the turtle a check-up in case there's a medical reason why she found him such a long way from his natural habitat. I pick him up and put him on my desk, and again he goes a bit haywire – he'd end up falling to the floor if I didn't redirect him.

'I think your mates got rid of you because you're a bit intense,' I say to him. 'They said, "We just need some space from your in-your-face antics."' However, as annoying as he might be, I'm still going to examine him. A patient is a patient, after all. And at least he isn't biting me!

I start by looking for fractures in his shell and injuries in the soft part of his body, but I find nothing. He's really in great shape. He's not even dehydrated – his eyes are very liquid, not at all sunken. Still I'm not quite ready to release him to the wild, so I take him home for a splash in Paddy the penguin's wading pool, as I don't know how long it's been since he's been in water. I want to observe him a bit longer to make sure he is okay.

A lot of people think that turtles have to live in water all the time; as a result, if they find one they whack it in a bucket of water. But this can be a bad thing for the turtle because being dry is quite good for them. People who keep pet turtles usually keep them in a tank with both wet and dry habitats to use as they need.

Mel's new little friend probably just got lost. Turtles like to migrate and they'll walk huge distances to new patches of water and new territory. And that's where they get themselves into trouble, especially when that 'exploring' involves crossing roads, where, given their far from express speed, the chances of getting hit by a car or cars is quite high. They're also quite partial to lying on warm bitumen as a way of warming their cold blood – again, not a great idea as cars tend to use warm bitumen too.

After watching him in the pool and giving him something to eat I'm quite satisfied this turtle is in no danger of suffering from anything other than a misguided sense of direction, so it's time to replace him in a habitat that's suitable for him. Sydney's Centennial Park has several lakes which support all sorts of fish, eels, ducks, ibis and other birds – and turtles. So I release the turtle into the reeds beside one of the larger lakes, and before I know it, he's gone.

A typical day at the clinic brings me a varied patient roster, and I find it constantly challenging – in a good way – because on any given day I have to be able to quickly treat any number of species and any number of problems.

However, there are some animals at the clinic who add to the variety but don't usually require any of my help, and they belong to the staff. As you'd expect from vets and vet nurses, we all have pets and the assorted staff pet collection is a veritable menagerie. I've already told you about my dog, Rusty. While he's a bit too shy to come to the clinic every day, most of the staff do bring their pets to work.

Tonya brings her ferrets, Baby and Jack, to work. She usually walks them to work, on a leash. It's quite a sight, I can assure you! Sara rides her bicycle to work with her dog in the basket. Neil arrives accompanied by his dog and Mel brings in her rat and her rabbit.

As Tonya says, 'It's awesome – we all get to hang out with each other. It's a really good environment.'

I hope everyone will continue to bring in their pets. Even though we work with animals, it's not the same as having your own pet there. I guess the nature of the 'office' we're in means that no one questions it when pets are brought to work, unlike some other workplaces. The value of pets in the workplace and even in places like hospitals and hospices has been documented – although I imagine a lot of offices would rather have dogs than ferrets! Still, having pets at work tends to improve morale in a workplace as other workers interact with the animal; it's good for the animal (particularly if it's a dog) as it's not pining for its owner at home; and it's good for the owner as they don't have to worry about their pet being home alone. Obviously there are little hiccups – it's hard to take your dog out for a toilet break if you're on the twenty-seventh floor – but I bet they're outweighed by the benefits, every time.

30

Curiosity Kills

Two nurses are now holding Zoe, the Bichon Frisé, as Dr Darren Foster tries yet again to insert a cannula into one of her veins. Zoe is suffering the effects of snakebite, and this is now causing a painful breaking down of her muscle tissue.

Having the extra nurse does the trick and Darren is successful. He injects antiserum into the cannula followed by methadone, which will alleviate some of Zoe's pain. The poison has not advanced far enough in Zoe's body for it to kill her and now that the antiserum has begun taking effect she should make a full recovery.

Zoe's case is a good example of the particular challenges of being a domestic animal in Australia. Just as we tend to think there are lots of things that can kill humans in this country – snakes, spiders, crocodiles, sharks – there are lots of predators for pets, too.

Lisa Chimes treated a lot of snakebites when she was studying emergency veterinary medicine in Melbourne, so I asked her whether she thinks there are special risks for Australian pets.

'If you ask the Americans,' she says, 'they'll say that Australia is full of venomous animals – the worst in the world! It's all scary! Australia does have its fair share of venomous animals, particularly on the East Coast and the coastal areas of the country. In the summer months, things like ticks and snakes would be the most common.

'There are also things like puffer fish and blue-ringed octopuses,' Lisa continues. 'People walk their dogs on the beach, and they're the most deadly creatures – animals that come into contact with either of those can die within ten minutes. Dogs get walked in bays or on beaches in shallow water, and the puffer fish blows up with all its spikes and dogs, being dogs, will go and have a sniff or maybe a little bite, and the toxin is a really powerful neurotoxin so it paralyses them. Within ten minutes to – if they're lucky – half an hour, if they're not treated they're dead. What those animals need is to be ventilated. They can be cured if you get them to a vet quick enough and they're put on a ventilator; within two days they can be better.'

As with a lot of pet health concerns, an aware owner is often the best form of prevention, as Lisa explains: 'If somebody's aware that going to the beach there's a risk of puffer fish and blue-ringed octopuses, then they would recognise the signs – the animal would vomit or just collapse straightaway – and the owner would know what it is and that they need to get it to a vet, or they need to give it mouth-to-nose resuscitation while they're taking it to the vet.

'With those venomous animals it's the education that's important, so people know what's out there and know what the risk areas and times are, and can recognise early signs of those problems – because most of those things, the longer you leave them the worse the outcome.

'So if the owner knows that they're in an area where there's brown snakes or tiger snakes and their animal's in the back garden and they're barking at something, and they come out and the dog's vomited and collapsed, then you have to use your head and say, "I'm in this area, that's what the dog's done, it's probably a snake – quick, we've got to get it to a vet." Whereas it's the people who aren't educated in terms of those venomous creatures who are the ones who delay in taking their animal to the vet, and that's when the outcome will be worse.'

There's one venomous creature that looms large in the consciousness of East Coast Australians in particular: the funnel-web spider. Some of you may even have seen your pet dog or cat with a funnel-web spider and been concerned about whether they'll get hurt (at the same time as you're worrying about not getting bitten yourself!).

Well, you can probably rest easy, as Lisa explains: 'I've never seen a dog that's been bitten by a funnel-web. In most situations when they've been bitten by a spider we wouldn't actually know it because the owner will bring them in for some sort of generalised reaction. You're not necessarily going to see the spider or see the bite. A friend of mine once had a funnel-web living in her rabbit's hutch and the rabbit lived with the funnel-web all its life. There are things that humans are more susceptible to that animals aren't.'

Pets and Snakebite

A dog's or cat's reaction to a snakebite depends on:

- The type of snake, as some snakes are more venomous than others.
- The amount of venom injected, which changes according to the size and age of the snake, the time of year at which the bite occurs (the start of summer is when snakes are most venomous) and the amount of time since the snake last bit something.
- Where on the body the dog or cat has been bitten; they are often bitten around the head and limbs – the closer the bite is to the heart, the faster the venom acts.

The usual signs of snakebite by a dangerously venomous snake (such as a brown or tiger snake) are:

- Sudden weakness followed by collapse.
- Shaking or twitching of the muscles.
- Vomiting.
- Dilated pupils not responsive to light.

Paralysis may occur in the later stages and the animal may have blood in its urine.

What should you do if your pet has been bitten?

1. Immobilise your pet and try to keep it as quiet as possible.

2. Go to a veterinary clinic or emergency animal hospital (like SASH) as quickly as possible. The faster your animal is treated, the better the chances of a good outcome.

3. Try to note the colour and approximate size of the snake, as this will help your vet to determine the right anti-venom to give your pet, but do not attempt to catch or kill the snake. Not only would you place yourself in danger, but you'd be breaking the law: snakes are protected species.

How does venom work?

When a snake bites an animal (or human) through the skin, the venom enters the lymphatic system which is much like the circulatory system in function. The venom is carried by the lymphatic system around the body, attacking the nervous system, damaging tissues and preventing the blood from clotting.

Survival and recovery

You must have your animal treated. Do not attempt to take care of your pet yourself. Eighty per cent of pets survive if they are treated quickly, but death is the likely outcome for an animal left untreated.

If treated promptly, it's possible for your pet to recover within twenty-four to forty-eight hours but some further care will be needed.

What is anti-venom?

Horses are the heroes of the anti-venom world – an anti-venom is produced by gradually immunising horses to the venom of certain species of snake. After a period of time blood is taken from the horses and the serum is separated and purified to make anti-venom. An anti-venom contains specific antibodies to toxins in snake venom.

Snake anti-venoms are costly – they are expensive to produce and don't last very long, so they're costly to replace too. Prevention is definitely the best form of cure, on a lot of levels.

Prevention

If you walk your dog in bushland (particularly near water) or near beach dunes during the warmer months of the year, keep them on a leash so they don't go chasing snakes.

If you live in an outer suburb or semi-rural area (or in the bush), keep the grass in your garden short and remove any garden rubbish. This will reduce the number of hiding places for snakes and thus make it less likely for your cat or dog to run across them.

Source: www.vetwest.com.au/snake-bite

31

The White
Rabbit

Fourteen-year-old Amy and her mother arrive at the clinic with Blackie, a three-year-old rabbit who is . . . white. Of course.

'What's wrong with Blackie?' I ask Amy.

'His fur's falling out in a clump,' she says. 'I was patting him and that chunky stuff comes off when you brush him.' She's referring to the combination of fur and skin that's on my fingertip.

'How long's he had it for?'

'Three weeks or so.'

I observed that Blackie had an almost bald patch right in the middle of his back – his fur is coming away and the area looks sore and itchy.

'You can see what's left here,' I say to Amy, 'that really dry, scaly skin. It's almost as though he's wearing a coat of talcum powder. You're lucky Blackie isn't black, otherwise he would have pretty obvious dandruff.'

Rabbits losing fur isn't that uncommon but the real trick will be working out the cause. It could be parasites; it could be a fungal infection; it could be an allergy. There's no way of knowing unless I run some tests.

First I ask Amy if she'd like to listen for Blackie's heartbeat, and when she tries there's an unexpected result: she tells me she can't hear it.

'It's more serious than we ever thought, then, isn't it?' Luckily, she giggles. No CPR is necessary for this rabbit just yet.

In the clinic there is all sorts of equipment for running tests – X-ray machines, endoscopes, pulse oximeters, ECGs, ultrasound machines, needles, stethoscopes . . . I need none of it to deal with Blackie. All I require is a humble piece of stickytape. Five years of university and all I can come up with is stickytape? But the tape really is all I need: I use it to pick up some fur and skin from Blackie.

Amy's not so sure about it, though: 'That hurts when you put a piece of stickytape on and pull it off,' she says. 'I feel sorry for him! I can't watch.'

I whip off the tape before she gets a chance to turn away but Blackie is not at all perturbed. In fact, he seems very relaxed about everything.

The tape goes onto a glass slide which I put under the microscope. Immediately I can see the problem: there are little fur mites and eggs hosting on Blackie's body. It's lucky Amy and her mum brought Blackie in while the problem was confined to one patch, because it could become much worse once those eggs hatch and the mites spread.

The contained location of the mites is simple enough to explain.

'What's the one place on Blackie's body that Blackie can't chew?' I ask Amy.

'Right in the middle of his back,' she says, quick as a flash. 'And that's where they've chosen.'

'You can see how many eggs there are. Very quickly this could go from being a small problem to being a very big problem. So what we're going to do is give Blackie a dog and cat treatment.'

Although rabbit mites are different to dog and cat mites, the same treatment can be used – it's a bit like a flea treatment – and it will take about twenty-four hours to have an effect.

Something else is having an effect on me, though – and unfortunately the treatment isn't as simple.

'Are you allergic to rabbits?' Amy's mother asks as she notices my right eye going red and I start to sniffle.

'Potentially . . .' I say

'Oops, sorry,' says Amy.

'It's only some rabbits.'

'Blackie, it's all your fault!' says Amy. 'How could you?' She pauses, trying not to smile. 'That's pretty funny.'

'It's funny, is it?' I say back to her. I can see the joke in the patient making me sick – even if it does mean I'll be sneezing for the rest of the day. Just put it down to an 'occupational hazard'.

I'm pleased we got a result for Blackie, even if he made me sick. If all my cases were so simple, I'd have a cruisy job – or maybe I'd just spend every day being allergic to my patients.

32

Motley

Though we have our share of dramatic cases at Bondi it really is nothing compared to the amount of emergencies the vets at SASH see. Lisa Chimes is working a shift when twelve-year-old Motley, a Shih Tzu cross, arrives at SASH in a very bad way. Lisa whisks her away immediately while one of the nurses takes some details from Motley's owners, Helen and Garry.

Motley is extremely limp – she has barely enough energy to lift her head, let alone walk or eat. Lisa starts a physical examination, and her first stop is Motley's mouth.

'As soon as you see white gums in a dog you know it's an urgent situation,' says Lisa. 'She's been bleeding in the gums. So any slight bump, she could bleed. She's really in quite a critical state.'

White gums mean that blood isn't circulating into the dog's head, so there could be something wrong with the heart. It can also be an indication of blood loss or shock. The fact that Motley's bruised in her gums is an additionally bad sign – not only isn't the blood properly circulating but when it *is* circulating, it's not clotting normally. Something is clearly very wrong with this dog, but Lisa doesn't know what. While she tries to find out, she puts Motley on oxygen to try to support the red blood cells in delivering oxygen to the tissues and hopefully help her feel a bit better.

One of Motley's owners, Helen, tells Lisa that Motley had surgery three weeks ago for a blocked gland, and just in the last few days some bruises have appeared on Motley's belly. Now Motley has bruises in her ears.

Says Lisa, 'It's possible that the antibiotics she was given after the operation have triggered an immune reaction which is basically attacking her platelets and causing her to bleed internally. We really are not able to stop the bleeding right now, but we can give her a blood transfusion to support her in the meantime.'

Motley's platelet count is four, which is extremely low. And where a blood count of thirty-seven per cent is the lower end of normal for a dog, Motley's is twelve per cent. Motley's condition is critical and she'll need a big blood boost in order to survive.

'Her immune system is going into overdrive,' says Lisa. 'It's breaking down her platelets and causing her to haemorrhage. Right now we don't know the exact cause but she needs a transfusion if she's going to make it through the night.'

Informed of the news, Garry, Helen's husband, says of Motley that she's 'a great little dog, a friendly little thing. Hasn't got a bad bone in her body. It's a sad thing, you know – it's part of your family.'

Lisa has to work out what is going wrong to have any chance of saving Motley, and she doesn't have a lot of time to do it.

33

Akasha

Akasha is a six-month-old Rottweiler pup with a very big problem: she is unable to stop urinating. She's not *making* herself urinate; rather, she has a physiological problem, a genetic deformity, which means that urine constantly trickles out of her. It makes life very hard for her owners, Matt and Mel. They live in Melbourne, where it can be very cold during winter, and Akasha's condition means she has to be an outdoors dog, because if she spends much time in the house Mel is constantly mopping down the floors. But they are worried that if she has to live outside all the time in a Melbourne winter, she's going to be a very unhappy dog. They want her to be able to roam in and out of their home and to be able to enjoy their dog without the huge amount of housework her condition now brings.

Matt and Mel adore their puppy and are trying as hard as they can to get her fixed, despite resistance from friends.

'A lot of people say to us, what's the point?' says Mel.

'It's only a hundred bucks to get them put down,' Matt says with a bitter tone, reflecting what they'd been told.

'Don't put up with it, they say,' Mel continues. 'We can't do that.'

'She's my little girl,' says Matt. 'I love her.'

Akasha needs a complex operation to correct her problem, and Matt and Mel want her to have it – but they don't have the 5000 dollars needed to pay for it.

'We were pleading to organise some sort of a payment plan,' says Mel. 'We could give a deposit upfront, go in there every week and obviously give them what we had. But no one would accept it.'

'I cried nearly every day, didn't I?' she says to Matt. 'It's just not fair on her and not fair on us.'

In desperation, Matt called a Melbourne radio station to tell them about the trouble he and Mel were having in finding someone to treat Akasha. The radio station put them in touch with me. Akasha's case was an extreme one – you don't see many dogs with these problems – and I wanted to do what I could. So I talked to the vets at SASH and they agreed to treat Akasha pro bono. Obviously they can't take on many cases free of charge, but they really wanted to help Akasha and were prepared to absorb the costs.

Now all Matt and Mel have to do is get Akasha to Sydney. And that would be one hell of a walk!

*   *   *

Matt is the one who accompanies his dog to Sydney. Akasha is bundled up into the cargo hold after Matt says goodbye. It is really important when you are sending your pet anywhere by air to prepare the animal for the trip. Make sure you have a very sturdy pet carrier and spend some time in the weeks before the flight getting your pet used to being confined in the cage. Akasha may not enjoy her trip too much but hopefully it will be a trip well worth making.

I'd already planned to meet Matt and Akasha before they went to SASH. I greet them at the airport and then we head to Bondi to give Akasha a chance to work off some energy before she goes into hospital. It's good to get dogs – especially young dogs – a little bit tired before they face a stressful situation like an operation. That way they're less likely to feel nervous. It works for humans too – think about how easily you relax or fall asleep when you're tired, as opposed to when you're feeling energetic. If you were facing a stressful situation, like a job interview, you'd probably feel less nervous if you'd run around the block beforehand. It's the same for Akasha.

Once Akasha has got her feet wet and met some curious local dogs, Matt and I head for SASH and Akasha's first meeting with Dr Andrew Marchevsky, who will be operating on her the next day.

Andrew Marchevsky is a specialist veterinary surgeon. He's the doctor who fixed golden retriever Rosie's front paws, and he's also the doctor who is best equipped to operate on Akasha's problem.

After Akasha arrives at SASH, and while Matt sits nervously in the waiting room, Andrew has some X-rays taken of Akasha's abdomen. The X-rays reveal that one of her kidney tubes is not connected to her bladder. Dogs (and humans) have two kidneys, which remove toxins and excess fluid from the body and produce urine as a result. Because Akasha's kidney tube is not going to her bladder she is unable to store it there and then control when she releases it. Instead the tube flows into her urethra, meaning she has had to put up with the constant trickle that she can't stop.

Andrew's plan is to cut off the kidney tube at the urethra, make a hole in the bladder and sew it on there. Andrew wants to make sure he's seeing the full picture – and to confirm that only one tube is faulty – so Akasha is given a diuretic to make her urinate faster and then she has her abdomen shaved in preparation for an ultrasound.

While he is looking at the ultrasound images, Andrew is surprised to discover that *both* of Akasha's kidney tubes aren't connecting to her bladder – the technical term is bilateral ectopic ureters. He's very concerned, as this dramatically increases the risk of complications from the operation. The surgery, quite painstaking and delicate just for one kidney tube, is now going to take quite a bit longer, which means more time under anaesthetic for Akasha and a greater risk of blood loss. Andrew is all too aware of what this will mean to Matt, too.

'They have got a very close bond,' he says of Matt and Akasha. 'He's moved heaven and earth to make sure that he can get his dog fixed. I think he'd be a bit of a mess if we have any problems.'

Andrew breaks the news to Matt about Akasha's true condition.

'We'll have to be very careful and monitor her kidney function and urine production,' he says of the operation. 'I know it's not quite the news you wanted. It's certainly not the news I wanted. But I guess that's why we did the tests. So now we know and I can prepare better for tomorrow.'

Matt is nervous but philosophical after Andrew leads Akasha away to be prepared for her surgery.

'She's all Andrew's now. Seems like he knows what he's on about – he's confusing me with the jargon! So we'll see what happens. But I'm pretty sure she'll be right. She'd better be.'

Privately, Andrew has his concerns.

'These problems are huge,' he admits. 'If you can't fix it she won't be able to be an inside dog. That'll increase the risk of getting infections . . . One of the options would be euthanasia for her, which would not be nice. That would break his heart.'

Akasha will be on the operating table for at least four hours, which is an extremely long time, even for a human. The longer an operation takes, the more difficult the job of the anaesthetist to keep the patient stable while they're unconscious. Breathing and blood levels all have to be monitored constantly, not to mention the anaesthetic itself, to make sure the patient is not awake or in any pain. Even with the best attention in the world, things can still go wrong – not from the operation, but because the animal is under anaesthetic for so long.

So Andrew is understandably feeling the weight of responsibility as he begins Akasha's operation. He is also keenly aware of how this situation could have been prevented in the first place. It turns out that Akasha's parents were related, a fact not known by Matt and Mel when they first took her home.

'It's a perfect example of why you shouldn't breed closely related animals to each other,' he says, because Akasha's deformity is the direct result of inbreeding.

After he's opened up Akasha's abdomen Andrew can see exactly what's going on. After four hours the problem has been fixed and the patient has come through the operation beautifully. Andrew still has some concerns that she may have some ongoing difficulty, but he's mainly positive about Akasha's prospects.

The next day Matt comes to visit Akasha, who is happy to see him – but it's the last she'll see of him for a few days. In order to keep his job, Matt has to return to Melbourne for work, and Akasha can't go with him yet. There is no way Andrew will discharge his patient until she's been able to urinate properly.

Matt is reluctant to leave Akasha behind but Andrew and the nursing staff are firm: Akasha's plumbing has to work before she's allowed to leave.

The good news is that after a couple of days Akasha is able to urinate properly. Andrew is delighted.

'It's amazing what you get excited about when you're a vet,' he says. I know just how he feels.

I made a promise to Matt and Mel that I'd personally escort Akasha home to Melbourne if Matt couldn't do it himself. I didn't want her going all the way to the airport and onto the plane without seeing a familiar face, even if she doesn't know me as well as she knows Matt. She's been through a lot in the past few days; if we can reduce her stress in any little way, it will make things easier.

When Akasha and I walk through Mel and Matt's back gate we find two very happy humans. Actually, make that three because I'll include myself in that. Akasha is a special dog and one of a kind in every way possible. I am very pleased to see her transformed by Andrew's work. Matt and Mel will now not have to worry about her getting any kind of urinary tract infection and they can keep her inside as much as they want. They have so much love for this dog that I know Akasha couldn't be in a better home.

34

Giving Blood

While Lisa and the team at SASH are doing all they can to help Motley improve, there's one thing they simply can't provide: the blood that Motley needs for a transfusion.

A commercially manufactured blood product is often used for animal transfusions – it is made out of red blood cells which are taken out of blood donated by dogs at an Australian university. Normally SASH would just order the blood, but if they run out of that then they have to find a donor.

Donor dogs have to be fairly big, preferably over twenty-five kilograms in weight, and the owner's consent is needed.

Says Lisa, 'We have one dog at SASH that is a Great Dane and the owner brings him in every six weeks just to donate blood. She wants him to be a blood donor.' But this

Great Dane is not on hand when Motley needs her blood. Nor does SASH have the blood products needed to transfuse the little dog.

Luckily for them all, Dr Justin Wimpole is still at work and he brought his dog, Milo, to work today. And Milo is a regular blood donor at SASH.

'He's a big boxer and really well behaved,' says Lisa. 'You don't need to sedate him too much.'

According to Justin, Milo has saved about a dozen dog's lives through his donations.'

There is no need for Lisa to find out if Motley and Milo have matching blood types before the transfusion begins, as dogs differ from humans in one important respect.

'Dogs have eight blood groups,' explains Lisa, 'but we actually don't have to match their blood types. Because of the way their antibodies work, they won't reject the blood on a first transfusion. So in Motley's case, she's never had blood before so we can get the procedure started straightaway.'

The vets and nurses at SASH do blood transfusions on dogs and cats all the time. 'It's a really common procedure,' says Lisa. 'Most vets also do it. I think some people are a bit more nervous about doing it if you haven't done a lot of blood transfusions. There is always a risk of a transfusion reaction, and in general veterinary practices that don't have overnight monitoring they wouldn't want to leave the dog having a blood transfusion while no one's there, so that's why they'll usually send them to a place like SASH. But certainly any vet is capable of doing it as long as you follow the right protocols.'

Cats are always 'a little bit trickier' to transfuse, says Lisa. 'With cats you always have to have a donor, because they don't commercially prepare cat blood. With cat blood you have to type them before you give them their first transfusion. We have a whole set of donor cats who live at the hospital. They have their own little bedrooms and stands and climbing things. We let them out to play. They have a pretty great life and all they have to do is donate blood once every few months.'

Milo isn't brought into SASH for the express purpose of donating blood, but it's very lucky for Motley that he is here tonight. As Lisa says, 'He's basically saving Motley's life. If we hadn't been able to collect the blood from him and give it straight to Motley, she may not have survived.' No wonder Milo gets a big treat once he's finished donating.

35

Bones

If you have a dog, you've probably given it a bone to chew on at least once in its life. In fact, you've probably been *advised* to give your dog raw bones – possibly to your cat, too. The theory is that as dogs and cats are natural hunters and, if left in the wild, would kill and eat their prey – bones included – then some raw bones are a normal part of a healthy diet.

It's true that raw bones are a good source of calcium, which, just as in humans, is essential for healthy bone development in dogs and cats. Bones can also be beneficial for their dental wellbeing – chewing on meat and bones keeps the animal's teeth and gums in good shape – and provide roughage for their digestive tract.

So far, so good . . . but you have to make sure that the bone is the right size for your dog. Or else your pet could end up in a situation like Ovis did.

Ovis is a springer spaniel who is brought into SASH with a bone wedged across his palate – the roof of his mouth. The edges of the bone are jammed against his teeth and his owners haven't been able to budge it.

Lisa is on duty when Ovis arrives. She has a look in Ovis's mouth while one of the nurses holds him still. The bone is wedged right back towards his throat, and he yelps a little bit as Lisa moves her hands towards his mouth.

'Generally dogs don't let you put your hands in their mouth,' says Lisa, 'particularly if there's something stuck in there and they're distressed about it. So, often they will have to be sedated for it – but Ovis seems like he's got a pretty good nature, so hopefully we'll be able to do it while he's conscious.'

Lisa uses a small pair of surgical scissors to try to grab the bone, but Ovis doesn't seem too impressed with her efforts. While he's not overly upset, he's none too happy either and not really holding his head still long enough for Lisa to get enough traction on the bone. It's enough to make Lisa think about sedating him, but she gives it one more go.

Putting her fingers on the bone, she attempts to pull it out.

'It's really stuck,' she says as the bone refuses to budge.

One of the SASH vets decides to help out and decides to push rather than pull – placing one finger on the top of the bone, he applies downwards force and the bone suddenly pops out – all the way to the floor.

Ovis is nonplussed, but Lisa is surprised by the condition of the bone.

'Look at that – it's pretty sharp on the edges!

'There's a bit of controversy over whether you give a bone to a dog,' Lisa continues. 'Definitely no cooked bones, and with raw bones I would be supervising the dogs while they're eating it and give them bones according to their size.'

Not only do cooked bones not have the same benefits as raw bones, but they're far more brittle – they can make your dog or cat's teeth much more blunt after repeated chewing, and they're more likely to break into the sort of large chunks like the one that became stuck in Ovis's mouth. If Ovis's bone had been a little bit smaller, he might have swallowed it instead – and that, too, would have required a trip to the vet, because if an animal swallows a cooked bone it can lead to colic, damage to the intestinal wall and constipation.

Ovis is lucky – his mouth is probably a bit sore, but that's the extent of the damage. It's a case of bad luck and good luck all at once: if the bone had been a bit bigger, it wouldn't have become stuck; if it had been a bit smaller, it might have ended up in his gut and caused far bigger problems.

Tips for Giving Bones to Your Dog

- Give large bones such as beef and lamb to large dogs only. Smaller dogs should not be given anything larger than a rib bone.
- Try to give your dog a bone with a bit of meat left on it, as this is a good 'workout' for the dog's canine teeth.
- Puppies should have a bone every day until they're about 12 months of age (for small dogs) and up to two years (for larger dogs).
- Adult dogs can have bones daily but don't need them as often – twice weekly is enough.
- Avoid cooked bones.
- Avoid bones that look small enough for your dog to swallow.
- Monitor your dog when it's eating a bone, to make sure the bone doesn't break into smaller pieces, which may then be swallowed (or become lodged in the dog's throat).

36

Check-ups

Thanks to Milo, Motley makes it through the night. The next morning she is well enough for Lisa to perform an ultrasound, but it turns out its results don't bode well for the little dog. Motley has chronic heart disease. The disease is so far advanced that the only thing to be done is to allow her to die peacefully, without trying to 'make her better' or sustain her further.

So often these hereditary diseases lurk in dogs, in particular. They are often the result of inbreeding, and this means that pedigreed dogs may die earlier than mutts. Still, there is a lot of information available about which dogs are prone to which diseases, so owners can keep themselves informed.

'I think nowadays people are pretty aware,' says Lisa. 'Hopefully we're doing our job as vets by trying to educate them. There certainly are breeds like Cavalier King Charles Spaniels and Boxers that generally will get heart conditions.

Whether or not you choose that breed is a difficult decision because their benefits – a Boxer and a Cavalier for example – can be great and there is a chance that your dog may not have a heart condition. It's a tough thing to weigh up.

'I'm a big fan of crossbreed dogs in terms of opening up the genetic pool. I've got a Cavalier crossed with a Poodle – I'm not allowed to say it's a 'cavoodle' because that's not an official breed. Poodles on their own are prone to skin diseases, and Cavaliers can have heart disease. Hopefully those genes won't mix in my dog. The theory is that you're opening up the genetic pool so there's less chance of genetic problems.

'Several decades ago there was much more inbreeding, I think, than there is now. I hope a lot of the breeders are more educated in terms of inbreeding and they realise the consequences of doing that. But there is going to be some degree of inbreeding in highly pedigreed dogs because that's just the nature of the practice.'

It's best to always be as informed as possible about the animal you're buying, whether it's a pedigreed dog or a budgerigar or a python. The more knowledge the owner has, the greater the likelihood that a pet can be integrated into the household with little drama and that the relationship between owner or family and pet will bring benefits to both sides. Too often dogs and cats are dumped after Christmas Day or when they're no longer young because they're not 'cute enough' anymore. If owners can make informed decisions about their pets this just won't happen so often – and that would make me and every other vet in Australia extremely happy.

It's also a good idea to have your pet checked over regularly, just like you'd go to the dentist or the doctor periodically. Obviously a check-up can't stop your animal developing a disease if it's genetically predisposed to one, but it can mean that the disease is anticipated and that it can be treated a lot earlier, so that your pet doesn't have to develop painful symptoms before something is done. Animals are generally fairly stoic – they can't complain about feeling sick the way we can, so they'll just quietly go off and eat grass or whatever they need to do to feel better. It can take a while for their owners to realise that something is wrong, and by that time it can be too late. If you're an informed pet owner who knows what conditions your pet is predisposed to develop then your vet can tell you what signs to look out for, and you can help make life a bit better for your littlest family member – and that will keep the humans happy too.

Dr Lisa Chimes has her own take on it.

'I always encourage people who tell me they are getting a puppy or whatever to learn about what it involves, even things like toilet training and walking and aggression, and all those kinds of behavioural things as well. People don't realise how much time and effort they need to put into their animal, and then the animal has problems and the owners say they don't want the pet anymore. They can hopefully reduce half their vet bills if they are aware of the particular illnesses the animal might get. If they're aware of flea treatments, tick treatments and checking for ticks and those kinds of things, then hopefully they can prevent themselves being hit with a big medical bill in the end.'

I think both Lisa and I would be happy to have fewer patients if it meant that owners were taking greater responsibility for their pets. As much as I like the challenge of an emergency case, I'd much rather have happy days at the clinic – and a well-cared-for pet is a happy pet with a happy owner.

37

Gentle Giants

Great Danes are the gentle giants of the dog world. Although they can seem intimidating – they're the tallest breed of dog in the world – I find they are usually pretty placid around humans.

Rufus and his son Yugul are both Great Danes, owned by Bondi local Ivo, who dotes on the pair. He takes the dogs for a swim in the surf every day – but somehow it's hard to imagine the wave that would topple a Great Dane. But today it takes something a lot smaller than a wave to bring Rufus down.

Ivo brings Rufus into the clinic, worried that he has been weak and losing his balance recently. Rufus also seems to be running a high fever.

While the fact Rufus is shaking his head and losing balance seems to back up my suspicions of an ear infection, I'm worried that it could be something else. I take a look inside one ear and it's a real mess – it's definitely inflamed and his ear canal looks red. Just to make sure, I extract some wax from the ear and it's black, which is not a great sign; it means there's probably an infection.

Because of the ear's proximity to the brain, there is a danger of the infection travelling down the ear canal, through his ear drum and into his brain, where it could cause meningitis. I'd like to rule this out as soon as I can, and I don't need an elaborate test: all I have to do is lightly tap Rufus's skull.

'I know it looks very strange,' I tell Ivo, 'but because meningitis is an inflammation of the meninges, which is the layer of cells that wraps the brain up, doing that hurts like hell. And for him to be able to put up with that, it's telling me that he doesn't have meningitis. The ear infection can develop into meningitis, though, but we're not there yet, and my goal is to prevent that from happening.'

Ivo had the same aim, but had a different approach: he gave Rufus human antibiotics. It's not good to give your pet any kind of human medication, especially antibiotics. Rufus could have been allergic to them, and a severe allergic reaction would have been enough to kill him. Apart from that, it's impossible to correctly estimate the dose a dog would need. For all the similarities between the body systems of mammals, there are significant differences and we all metabolise certain substances differently. Even a human and a dog of similar body weight will not need the same dosage of medications.

Luckily giving the antibiotics doesn't look to have caused too many problems, and I can give Rufus an injection of antibiotics to stop the infection in its tracks. He should start to improve within the next forty-eight hours.

Sometimes we can become so attached to our pets – especially the warm-blooded ones – that we think they're 'just like us'. We extend that thinking to their health – we try to interpret their symptoms to match those of a human illness. Certainly, there are some conditions and diseases that mammals share, and our body systems all work similarly. But that's the extent of it. Our pets will rarely express pain or show symptoms the way humans will, and they certainly can't tell us where they hurt – so it's impossible to know exactly what's wrong with them just by comparing them to humans.

If you think your pet is sick, then it probably is, and it's best to get it checked out at your local veterinary clinic. 'Better safe than sorry' is a good motto to live by.

Did You Know?

The title of the tallest dog belongs to Gibson the Great Dane, who stands at 107 centimetres tall.

38

Blackie
the Cat

'What's happened to your leg, mate?' I ask the little black kitten who's arrived with a very agitated owner. Michael has brought in the kitten – named Blackie – who belongs to his elderly parents. Blackie is a mere eight months old, but he appears to be suffering from a very grown-up injury.

'He disappeared for a day and a half,' Michael tells me, 'and all of a sudden he rocked up on the back porch. He was meowing, actually. Dragging himself in.' Michael looks distressed, and I can't blame him: first the kitten disappears and then he reappears with what looks like a fairly major problem. The stress of worrying about him would get to anyone with a heartbeat.

'So you have no idea what's happened?' I ask. 'It doesn't look like there's any blood, at least.'

'What do you think's wrong with him?' Michael asks.

'It's hard to say, mate. It could be anything.' And that is the truth. I have to examine every animal I see very carefully to come up with a diagnosis. But hopefully there are signs that lead me the right way.

Blackie's front legs are working fine but his back legs are worrying me – they're hanging limply. As I feel along the limbs, Blackie struggles.

'It's all right, Blackie,' I say, trying to soothe him. I'm not sure it works. It's imperative that I diagnose him quickly so I can treat him immediately. I keep palpating his legs, trying to work out the extent of the problem.

'He's certainly either damaged the ligaments or has a fracture there,' I tell Michael.

'Just as long as he's going to be okay,' says Michael. 'He just means so much to us.'

'He's your parents' cat?'

'Mum and Dad's cat, yeah. I spend a bit of time with him as well. He's very close to the family . . . He's very important to us, mate – I just hope he's going to be okay.'

I'm hoping for the same thing, but the longer I examine Blackie, the more doubts I have. His back legs are an absolute mess. The right leg is just hanging there, and appears to have no sensation – Blackie doesn't respond to my attempts to create a pain response – and there is no movement whatsoever. But it's his left leg that I'm more interested in. If that leg can't be salvaged, if it is in serious trouble – then Blackie has no hope. He needs at least three working legs; he wouldn't be able to function with just two.

I feel along his back left leg and manipulate it a bit to see if there's any pain there. Pain would be a good sign – not only is it the body's way of saying that something's wrong and that you shouldn't go any further, but in Blackie's case pain would tell me that his nerves are still connected in that leg. The absence of pain in his right leg suggests that the nerves there are gone, and it would be very difficult to restore them.

There's a certain crunchiness in Blackie's left hind leg – it's the sound of a fracture. Blackie squirms as I press a bit harder. I don't want to but I have to in order to work out what's wrong.

'It's all right, mate,' I say.

'I'd say he's got a fracture,' I tell Michael. 'And the fact is that if he can't straighten that leg he can't support weight on it.' I'm trying to prepare him for the realisation that Blackie may never walk properly again.

Having a closer look at Blackie's paws, another piece of his puzzle appears. I show the paws to Michael.

'Wherever he's dragged himself from, he's worn down the nails just in an effort to get home to you,' I tell him. 'Blackie, you're a tough little guy, aren't you?'

I'm filled with admiration for this young cat. He has clearly been through an enormous ordeal; he's shown bravery by dragging himself back to his family, and considering the extent of his injuries he's been relatively stoic while I've examined him. He's clearly a fighter, and that bodes well for his ability to recover.

Michael tells me a bit more about his family's beloved pet: 'Blackie's the kind of cat that needs to be around humans all the time. He loves the pats and the attention. He's just a beautiful cat and gets on with everyone.

'He's a baby that needs a lot of love and attention, that's for sure. Mum and Dad are really concerned. They're very attached to him. They love him lots.'

Every time I treat a pet I'm fully aware of the emotional attachments that go with the animal. I'm not just taking care of the pet; I'm taking care of everyone who cares about it. It's a big responsibility, and in Blackie's case I feel it even more keenly. He's a very young cat with very devoted owners. He's also a young cat with a great deal of damage to his body.

Not only does Blackie seem to have two badly fractured hind legs, the nerves to his tail appear to be dead. When I examine him and feel around the tail and legs, he should be thrashing around and his tail should be hitting me – but it's limp and lifeless. If both legs and his tail aren't working properly, he won't be able to go to the toilet as the nerves that control that function come from the same part of the spinal cord; if he can't go to the toilet he can't really live. Or, rather, it would be inhumane to allow him to live in that condition.

'You're a tough little fella, aren't you?' I tell him while Michael looks on.

As Blackie is only eight months old, youth is definitely on his side. His bones are also quite flexible because he's so young, and that means he's not quite as damaged as he would have been if his bones were brittle; an impact on a brittle bone is likely to shatter it. And it's clear that something large has made an impact on Blackie – we just don't know what.

Michael is beside himself with worry. I want to reassure him, but at the same time I don't want to give him false hope.

'Mate, we'll do everything we can,' I tell him, 'because I know how much he means to you. I guess, looking at what he's been through and the effort he's made to get home . . .'

'He's a special cat, Chris. I'm going to leave him in your hands, mate, so you can make him better.'

'We'll do everything we can.'

'How soon can you tell about the nerves?' Michael asks me.

'We can run a few tests, but the most important thing is this X-ray. We need to take the X-ray and work out whether there's nerve damage and where the breaks are in his legs. So the first priority is to work out where he is medically and then really work out if we can do something.'

'When do you think you'll get results?'

'I'll do it straightaway.'

'It would be very difficult if we lost him. Do the best you can for us, mate.' Michael turns to Blackie as I feel the weight of hope from Michael and his parents.

'Okay, mate, you'll be fine,' he tells the beloved kitten. 'You're a strong cat, don't forget that.' And with a kiss and a pat of Blackie's head, he's gone.

39

Mr Wilson

Some pets have all the luck: they are adored by their owners and treated so much like 'one of the family' that they almost seem to have a seat at the dinner table.

In the case of Mr Wilson, that dinner table would be in his owners' Chinese restaurant in Batemans Bay on the South Coast of New South Wales.

Four-month-old Mr Wilson is the beloved pet Shar-Pei of John and Fiona, who have closed up their restaurant for the day and driven four hours to Bondi just so I can have a look at him: they're friends with the parents of one of my flatmates, and clearly she's been doing a bit of referral business . . .

Like all Shar-Peis, Mr Wilson is covered in wrinkled folds of skin – it's the breed's most distinctive characteristic – but in Mr Wilson's case there's a bit too much skin: so much in fact that his eyelids have begun to roll back onto his eyeballs, causing irritation and infection. He's still a puppy, so it's likely that the effects on his eyes could become considerably worse as he grows up and he could potentially lose his sight.

John and Fiona have absolutely no problem with how Mr Wilson looks – they think he's gorgeous – but they are worried about his eyesight being obscured. And Mr Wilson is clearly so important to them that they're prepared to do a lot to see him fixed.

'She calls him "my son",' says John, laughing, 'and I call her "Grandma" when I'm talking to him.'

'He's the number one part of the family,' confirms Fiona. 'He's my baby. You've got to treat them like your kids.'

When John and Fiona arrived in Sydney they went straight to Bondi Beach, before they came to the clinic. John hadn't been to Sydney before; obviously, neither had Mr Wilson. But he quickly made friends as the trio strolled the beach strip: several people stopped John and Fiona to ask about Mr Wilson.

Now they're at the clinic, telling me about their restaurant.

'What's your most popular dish?' I ask them.

'Rainbow beef,' says John, and it gives me an idea . . .

'Got any with you right now?' I ask, smiling. 'We could do a bit of a contra arrangement.'

John laughs. 'We'll see what the result is first, shall we?'

'What time did you have to get up this morning?'

'We got up at two-thirty.'

'If I got up at two-thirty I'd look like Mr Wilson!' I say, laughing.

John laughs again. 'They say I already do.'

Mr Wilson just snorts.

'Now, obviously you're worried about his eyes,' I say to John.

'This one mainly, it's not opening as much as the other one.'

'Does he have trouble seeing?'

'Yeah, sometimes he can't play with the ball – he can't see where it is – and he's always bumping into chairs and tables.'

Mr Wilson snorts again – in fact, there's been a bit of a snort soundtrack throughout the consultation, so I need to ask John some more questions.

'Does he snort often?'

'Constantly,' John replies. 'You have no idea.'

'I can see the attraction,' I say, smiling. 'The looks, the quiet sound – they make a very appealing breed.'

'Oh yeah,' says John, but I can tell he really *does* think that Mr Wilson is appealing despite the fact that the animal is a snorer too.

'Is the snoring worse at night?' I ask.

'Yes,' replies Fiona. 'Worse than this one.' She points at John. 'You can hear him from the next room.'

'John, is this fair?' I say.

'That's how it is,' John says, looking rueful. 'I'm number two, not number one.' He laughs, though, and I suspect that Mr Wilson is the centre of John's universe too. But now it's time to get to the serious business.

'I can see a couple of issues here,' I say to John and Fiona. 'Certainly his eyes aren't wide enough open – he's got pretty obvious vision deficits. He just can't see because his eyes are crowded over by the skin.

'The other problem is that he's got what's called entropion, which means he has so much loose skin that the eyelashes roll inward and they sit on the actual eyeball itself. It's like having an eyelash stuck on your eye the whole time – it feels like sandpaper. To a certain extent he will grow into his face, so it's probably at its worst at the moment. But the problem is that if we leave it alone he's going to get permanent eye damage and he would run a real risk of blindness.'

That's not the full extent of the situation, though.

'The other issue is that he's quite young and we've got anaesthetic issues with a young dog, so we need to be very careful. But at the same time we need to act.'

Mr Wilson needs an eyelift, and for him it's definitely not a cosmetic procedure. In the operation I'll lift up the affected eyelid, pull down the bottom eyelid and perhaps take a slice out of the corner, and thus make his eye a little bigger – and allow the eyeball to see the world more clearly. It will also possibly be the first time Mr Wilson will get a good look at John and Fiona.

To lighten up the worried expressions that have settled on Fiona and John I ask them . . .

'While we're in there, you don't want any changes, do you? I can do anything you like. Do you want a nose job as well? In fact we could turn him into anything you like. How about a Pomeranian?'

Fiona looks both horrified and amused at once. 'I'm quite happy with my baby!' she says, a little indignantly.

Shar-Peis can have a reputation for being aggressive dogs. Originating from China, they were bred as hunting and guard dogs. The point of all those loose folds of skin is to help them with their hunting. If another animal grabs hold of them, it just gets the skin and not the dog – so the floppy covering works as a defence mechanism. During the Communist regime people were trying to breed out the Shar-Peis – they nearly became extinct. But they lived on and Mr Wilson is the proof.

I've met a lot of Shar-Peis who belie their fighting dog roots and are actually very sweet with an easy-going temperament. It is not hard to see that Mr Wilson falls into that category. And he'll be even easier to be around when he's under anaesthetic.

Wrangling him into position to administer the anaesthetic is a little less fun – Nurse Mel has the job of holding onto him while he snorts away. Mysteriously, she also finds him beautiful. Clearly there's something I'm missing. I think Shar-Peis are . . . *unique*. It's possible for a dog to be so far down the ugly scale that it loops around to the beautiful scale, and Mr Wilson is the epitome of that. I also have to admit I find him highly entertaining – he is one of those spontaneously amusing dogs you can't help but look at and laugh.

It also turns out that Mr Wilson, like many teenage boys, is a bit of a sook – before the needle gets anywhere near his skin, he yelps and barks at Mel and me.

'Oh Mr Wilson, come on,' I tell him. Maybe he comes to his senses as I'm able to slip the needle in – and he doesn't even notice! The fact that he's crying must be caused by something else.

'Is this dog spoilt by any chance? Mel asks.

'Why do you say that?'

'The fact that he's crying for Mum and Dad. He's been inconsolable since they left.'

We almost feel sorry for him. But there's still an operation to perform, and I'm now acutely aware that I'm not treating just a dog: I'm treating a semi-human dog. He's even called 'Mr Wilson'. So there's a lot riding on this procedure. Fiona and John expect the best and I'll be doing my utmost to make sure they get it.

I start by putting fluorescent dye into Mr Wilson's eyes to check that there are no ulcers on their surface. Because his eyelashes have been rubbing on his eye so much they could have taken off an outer layer of the cornea, which can cause great pain. If any ulcers have developed they will glow bright green when I turn off the light.

I'm pleased to see that Mr Wilson's eyes are not glowing in the dark. So there's one less thing to worry about.

What *is* worrying me is the anaesthetic we'll have to give him. Because he's quite young we have to make sure we get his levels right – that he's neither too deeply unconscious nor too conscious – because he doesn't have the body mass or the maturity to metabolise the anaesthetic the way an adult dog would.

Once Mel and I are satisfied that Mr Wilson is safely asleep, I get to work on his right eye. I'll have to put a row of stitches on his upper and lower eyelids, essentially pulling the skin apart, and that should open his eyes right up. I can't move the skin too far without causing problems, but it's quite hard to get the balance: Mr Wilson's skin bounces around a lot, making it very difficult for me to make the incision. It's a bit like jumping on the corner of a water bed – the moment you hit it his skin flies to the other side of his face and the moment I take my hand away the skin comes back. I've never performed an operation like this on this sort of dog before and it all seems a bit strange, not to mention imprecise: I have to estimate how much eyelid I can take, then put the stitch in. If it doesn't look right, I'll have to remove the stitch and try again. So it's frustrating, but also fascinating in its own way.

Once the right eye looks good, I move to the left, which is more troublesome as the skin is drooping far more on this side, so I'm worried about taking too much skin, not too little. I don't want Mr Wilson ending up looking permanently startled like a Hollywood actor who's developed

225

a cosmetic surgery addiction – well you know what I mean . . .

The delicate surgery takes two hours, and at the end I'm happy with the result. I've put three stitches on the bottom left eyelid and four at the top, and the skin has been pulled upwards and downwards, revealing more of his eyeball. The big test will be when Mr Wilson is conscious – because he's still asleep everything is falling down with gravity. When he wakes up I want to see his eyes springing to life with twenty-twenty vision. That may not happen for a few days, however, because there will be a bit of swelling. Mr Wilson's red-carpet moment will have to wait.

Mr Wilson's stitches will be staying in for three months, until he reaches seven months of age – because by then he'll have literally grown into his skin. That's a fair way off, though, and for now I'm just pleased that he's recovering well from the operation. Mr Wilson seems pleased too, offering me lots of snorts and snuffles while I examine him later that afternoon.

The next day I arrive early to check him one last time. I have to say, he looks like a very happy chap – he genuinely looks as though it's the first time he's seen the world and he's in awe of it – his tail is wagging vigorously. It's lovely to watch.

Neil is standing by while I examine Mr Wilson. For some reason he's the recipient of lots of kisses from our wrinkly patient – all I get is snorts. That'd be right – I do all the work and get none of the glory. Although there may be a good reason for it, maybe he's had a personality change because he can now see strangers and the world around him, whereas before he was a little bit introverted and withdrawn because of the fact he couldn't see anything. Perhaps now the real Mr Wilson has been revealed.

John and Fiona arrive to see their boy, and it sounds like it's been an anxious night – it turns out they've never been separated from him before.

'I was missing my baby,' says Fiona. 'I always think what's it going to be like – I should have left a jumper for him so he could have felt that I was beside him. I can't wait to see him.'

They are over the moon to be reunited with the now-gregarious Mr Wilson.

'Give Mummy a kiss!' says Fiona. 'Give Chris a kiss!'

'So I was thinking,' I say to Mr Wilson, 'for your last check-up I might come to Batemans Bay for a Chinese meal and see how you're going.'

Mr Wilson snorts and wags his tail. Hopefully he'll be as happy to see me in six weeks' time, when he needs a check-up. Until then, he'll be the most glamorous Shar-Pei in Batemans Bay.

40

Fingers Crossed

Blackie the kitten is in a very bad way and it's imperative that I take an X-ray of him to work out if there are definitely fractures and, more importantly, if his spinal cord is affected. I think his right leg is completely paralysed, and the fact that his tail isn't moving is an extremely bad sign – it suggests that he may have sustained some nerve damage, and I need to know how extensive it is. I also really want confirmation that his left leg can be rescued. If he has three functioning legs, he can get by. If he has just two, then the only option is to put him to sleep. This is an option I'm hoping I won't have to discuss with Michael.

Once I've taken the X-ray, Sara looks after Blackie while I check the films. I'm almost holding my breath waiting to discover the extent of his injuries. Of course I don't want them to be bad, but at the same time I want to know exactly what's going on so I can treat it.

Then, unexpectedly, Sara's uniform begins to move in the vicinity of her chest.

'What's that?' I ask her.

'It's a baby possum,' she tells me with a smile. 'I'm warming him up. He came in from the cold.'

Nothing is surprising in a vet clinic! I'd seen the possum earlier and he had been cold. Sara's solution to the problem is a good one and, as she puts it: 'We have to multi-task in this place and in all seriousness we have to get him warm. Once he's warmed up we'll get him some glucose.'

Of course, she's right. And the possum's challenges are mild compared to Blackie's. The X-rays tell me the whole sad story: he has so many things wrong with him that I have to weigh up if it is worth doing anything more. Blackie's determination and the family's attachment are one side of the story but the quality of life that Blackie can expect has to be my key concern. These can be heart-breaking decisions but, if I can, I will do everything to give him a chance.

41

Flight of the Falcon

Near the clinic there's a massive shopping centre called Westfield which seems to be busy from dawn till midnight. It's a sprawling complex housing department stores, restaurants and cinemas – and, it turns out, a family of peregrine falcons who have been living at the top of the main tower for five years. These birds of prey are one type of animal that I very rarely see up close. There's not really much opportunity to treat them in the wild, and even less in the city.

We receive a call from Bruce Campbell, the security manager at Westfield. Since the clinic is just around the corner, I get to the centre quickly and Bruce meets me there.

'I'm pleased to see you,' he says by way of greeting, then shows me the reason for the call. 'This is a falcon from upstairs. We found him at the base of the towers. He looks really weak. You can see how he's laying down. He just let us catch him. He's a peregrine falcon. I know there's a pair of them up there.'

'How did you catch him?' I enquire.

'He was just floundering around,' says Bruce. 'He looked crook, mate, and he looked like he had some damage. His wings were really weak.

It turns out this falcon wasn't found just anywhere. This most efficient of killing machines was found in the complex's child-care centre. Luckily no child thought it would be nice to hand-feed this giant pigeon!

'We got a fruit box,' Bruce continues, 'and placed it over the top of him and slipped another piece of cardboard under him and picked him up. He gave no struggle, which worries me even more. The odd thing was that his eyes were alert but he was very placid – he didn't even screech.'

I'm amazed that Bruce has managed to catch the falcon. These birds are fierce and strong – they are perfectly designed birds of prey that can fly at a speed of over 380 kilometres per hour – and ordinarily the bird would have fought hard against a human trying to put it in a box. They have two weapons of choice: their very powerful beak, which would shred a human hand if it got too close and their long, knife-like claws or talons.

These birds are such powerful, graceful creatures that I'm very concerned to see this falcon looking so placid.

'This is their building,' Bruce tells me now. 'They live here. I just work here. And this one's part of the family. The cleaners have named him – that's either Frank or Judy. We don't know which one.'

I tell Bruce that I'll need to take the falcon – Frank or Judy – back to the clinic for treatment.

'His mate's up there,' Bruce says, 'and he's very important to us.' Apparently there are chicks in the nest, too. 'We have heard the babies up there, but we haven't heard them for the last couple of days.'

Frank – I've decided that he's Frank until proven otherwise – looks like a young adult from his plumage. Why he's so sick, though, is harder to determine. I really need to get this bird back to the clinic quickly.

'Keep in touch, please,' Bruce says. 'Keep me posted, because he's a very special bird, this one.'

'Well done catching him,' I say, still amazed he has all his fingers.

'Take care, Doc. Catch you soon.'

Once I get Frank back to the treatment room he is so uncharacteristically still that I have no trouble doing a physical examination. I weigh up the possibilities as I go. He could have flown into a window or past something and clipped it with his wing. Though I don't think either would explain his docile nature.

Suddenly Frank starts to screech and flap his wings, startling me and Sara, who's assisting me.

'Shh, it's all right,' I tell him, 'I'm trying to help you.'

I don't want to distress him further, but I need to stretch out his wings to have a good look at them. Frank puts up a bit of a fight, but I don't think it's because he's in pain and I am pleased to see a bit of spirit. I can't see any damage to his wings, which is such important and good news . . . for now.

The fact that Frank was found hopping around on the ground, and that he allowed himself to be caught by a human, is of the greatest concern – these falcons very rarely come down to the ground because they're such great flyers. So why would he stop doing what he's born to do? It's really puzzling me: there's no damage to his wings; his legs seem to be fine. He's a little on the skinny side, but there's nothing obvious that would be making him so ill that he couldn't fly.

We take an X-ray just to be sure; it reveals that nothing is broken. Now I start to think about his internal organs and systems.

My nagging concern is that peregrine falcons live at the top of the food chain – they pick off everything underneath them. Their main source of food is pigeons, which eat almost anything. And pigeons come across a lot of poison – in fact, in the past it has been shown that some businesses poison pigeons to keep their numbers down.

If Frank has eaten a poisoned pigeon, or a number of them, that could be enough to weaken his system and bring him to a point where he can no longer fend for himself, let alone his chicks.

It's also possible that he's suffering nothing more sinister than exhaustion and malnourishment. Living in the city would be quite tough for a falcon – there wouldn't be paddocks full of potential prey for them so he would have to work a lot harder to survive. He could very well be eating prey he just shouldn't.

Frank is finally showing some vigour – and directing it at me. I'm trying to examine his mouth and he really doesn't want me to. In fact, he's so unhappy about it that he tries to bite me.

As soon as I see in his mouth I get an important clue. 'This looks like a big plaque of thrush,' I say to Sara. 'It's a classic sign of a stressed immune system. The thrush just grab their opportunity and take hold. The problem is that it makes feeding difficult and compromises their throat.'

'That could be our problem right there.'

I need to get a swab from Frank's mouth to confirm the diagnosis and that's a *lot* easier said than done. Sara tries to hold him still while I put a cotton bud in his mouth.

'Watch his talons,' I say, and then Frank grabs Sara's fingers with one of his claws. Frank fights us both, pushing me away as I try to get closer. I finally manage to get a swab, but poor Sara has paid the price.

Now I have evidence of a condition that may be causing at least part of Frank's weakness, I can treat him, so for the next few days he'll be the lucky recipient of anti-fungal medication and antibiotics via syringe twice a day. And someone – probably me – will have to risk losing fingers to put the syringe in his mouth.

We also need to make sure he's eating properly. In the wild falcons eat four or five times a day, so Frank will need to be fed small amounts to build up his reserves of energy – mince and steak should give him all the protein and fat he needs.

While we're trying to take care of Frank, there's still the matter of his mate and chicks at the top of the tower. If Frank is in this kind of shape, it's likely they're not healthy either.

There's also the matter of working out whether Frank really is Frank – or Judy. Male and female peregrine falcons look identical, except the females are bigger. The only way to tell whether Frank is male is to see him next to the other falcon. Fundamentally, whether we're dealing with Frank or Judy doesn't matter – both peregrine parents have to work together to feed chicks, and as there's only one parent left in the tower, the chicks may not survive much longer.

We have to work out a way to get to those chicks and in the meantime we'll keep Frank in overnight.

42

Fractured

Michael is waiting for me in a treatment room when I return from taking X-rays of Blackie.

'Mate, what he's been through and the injuries he has are just astonishing,' I say.

I hold up the X-rays for him to have a look.

'See here – he's fractured his right femur – his right leg – basically where it inserts in the hip joint. It's rammed right through.'

Michael looks even more worried than he did before. But I have to tell him the true extent of Blackie's injuries.

'The problem with this break being so bad is the fact that when that bone snapped and ended up so far away from where it should be, it took the nerves with it. That's why his leg is outstretched and has no feeling and no movement.'

'Poor thing,' says Michael, and he's not wrong.

I show him the X-ray of the left leg for a comparison – it's a 'normal' leg.

'If you go across to the bad one – the right leg that's hanging limply – that's where the femur should be yet it's right up there, pushed right through the hip.

'The problem with that – and I'm not going to mince my words – is that if it's gone through and torn the nerves like we think it has, we can't regrow those nerves.' I take a deep breath before I continue. 'He's never going to walk again with a leg like that.'

'So what are you saying?' Michael asks. 'We're going to have to get rid of the leg?'

'I know it's hard to take, but yes, we're going to have to amputate that leg.'

'It just puts it into perspective, what he's done to get home, dragging two broken legs.'

'He's a fighter, mate, that's for sure.'

Telling anyone that their much-loved pet is going to lose a leg is one of the toughest jobs a vet has, but when that pet is just eight months old . . . It's an awful situation, and I can understand why Michael is so upset. But there's a positive aspect to this: Blackie is young and he has a beautiful, gentle personality. He's the perfect cat apart from these injuries. And, all going well, I can salvage his other leg so he can learn to move on three legs and end up living fairly normally. I'll do what I can to make sure he has as good a life as possible. Though there are no promises and it will be a very serious operation with extensive recuperation necessary I think Blackie has a good chance of pulling through. I wouldn't suggest this option if I didn't think it was going to work.

'I'm happy to accept that,' Michael says finally, 'but Mum and Dad might find it a bit difficult.'

'I guess when the alternative is putting him to sleep, it's better than that.'

'We definitely can't do that. He's just too special.'

I explain to Michael that, apart from amputating Blackie's right hind leg, I'll need to fully reconstruct his left.

'To give him any chance at all – and we're still talking slim chances – we've got to repair this left leg here as well. We need to put some pins in to stabilise that fracture. If we don't . . . I'm sorry to say there's nothing we can do.'

'At the end of the day, if it's for his own good, then we have to give him a chance,' Michael replies.

I wish that were the extent of the bad news I have to deliver to Michael, but I'm still puzzling over just how Blackie ended up in this state. I have a theory, and I need to tell Michael.

'The issue I've got with this whole scene is the fact that when cars hit cats they do massive damage – fractured ribs, internal injuries, plus they tend to crush the pelvis as well. Blackie's injuries are coming from the back. Something's happened here to rip that femur out of the joint from its base.

'I guess I don't like to jump to conclusions but whatever's happened to Blackie has taken him from the back with a farily precise upward force. To my way of thinking, it's a deliberate act. I think Blackie's been kicked from behind – for a laugh, a cheap shot to impress mates . . . I don't know, but it sickens me.'

I think the seriousness of what I'm telling Michael only just sinks in and he swallows. 'What are his odds?'

'Well, I guess if Blackie can drag himself the whole way home just to give himself a chance of living, then you can be pretty sure we've got one hell of a fighter here.'

'I just hope he's okay,' says Michael. 'I'll be praying for him.'

43

Frank
and Judy

Frank the peregrine falcon has spent the night in the clinic, although not quite next to the cat cages. We didn't think it would be fair on the cats, looking at those talons all night.

Sara and I go to check on him in the morning.

'Good morning, Frank. Good to see you staring at me again.'

'He looks a lot better, doesn't he?' I say to Sara. 'Feistier.' Accordingly, I don a glove before I open the cage.

'Look how pretty he is,' says Sara.

'He's a hired killer.'

'He's not! He's magnificent.'

As I remove Frank from his cage he's sounding a lot happier – chirping instead of shrieking.

'He's saying, "Feed me, I'm hungry",' Sara says.

I'm happy that Frank is a lot more alert and showing considerably more spark than yesterday, even if he shows it by pecking at my finger. He's also extremely interested in the meat we're giving him – yesterday food didn't seem so important to him, but now he seems to instinctively want to build up his energy reserves plus he's enjoying the calcium supplements we're also adding in. It's a great sign.

As we offer Frank the meat, he stops his squawking and grabs it.

'That's one way to keep you quiet,' I say.

'I think we can confirm that he's a male,' says Sara. 'Food keeps him quiet plus he's mouthy.'

I'm not so sure about Sara's method of deduction, especially as Frank's no longer quiet – he's trying to grab at the meat, squawking while he's eating. The gloves are proving to be inadequate protection against a hungry falcon – he's doing a bit of damage to my fingers while I'm feeding him and I'm not looking forward to feeding him again over the twenty-four to forty-eight hours needed for him to build up enough strength to be returned to his habitat. But as much as I value my fingers, I don't want to send him back too early and risk him becoming weak again.

Frank is still voraciously enjoying his food.

'It's the cheapest chuck steak we could find,' I tell him, 'but I'm pretty sure – and I can't back this up with fact – that it's tastier than pigeon.'

Unbelievably, while we're trying to keep Frank in steak, we receive another call from security at Westfield: they've found

Frank's mate, Judy, in the same child-care centre showing the same signs. She's delivered to us in a cardboard box.

'It looks like her,' I say. 'She's meant to be looking after the babies and . . .' The box starts rattling. 'She's a tough woman!' Judy is trying very hard to get out of the box – she's in much better shape than Frank was when he first came into the clinic.

'You've got a bit more go than your husband,' I tell her. As she looks a bit bigger than Frank, I think I'm safe saying 'her'. 'What's going on with you, miss? Why are you here as well?'

I examine Judy as best I can and determine that she's not able to fly either. She's also very weak, but putting up more of a fight than Frank did. She goes for me and gets in a bite, at which I let out a bit of a yelp. In a masculine way, of course.

'I'd never say this in front of Frank but I get the impression she's the breadwinner of the family.' Frank is really looking like a walkover compared to this wild child! And then, as if to prove the point, she bites me again. 'She gets those talons and beak right into you. But despite the fact she's fighting hard, she really doesn't have much to her. She's skin and bone.'

I'm prepared to look past the fact that she's using me for target practice and appreciate the extraordinary fact that she's here at all. Having one falcon at the clinic has been incredible; to have two in two days is truly remarkable. We've had all sorts of wildlife in the clinic before but never any birds of prey like this. I just hope we can take care of them properly and return them to the wild, or Westfield, soon.

Judy is not displaying the same symptoms of thrush as Frank, though they do have other problems in common, and I still believe that pigeons have something to do with it.

I take Judy to see Frank but it's not quite the romantic reunion I was expecting. Judy is looking at Frank as if she's found him spending the kids' school tuition at the local casino. I suspect that once I turn off the lights and leave them alone, Judy will be having serious words with Frank about where he's been for the last twenty-four hours and why she's had to look after the kids all by herself. And I have to say, I feel sorry for Frank. I'd hate to be on the wrong side of this woman.

Judy needs to take some antibiotics and anti-fungals just in case she's harbouring the same kind of nasties as Frank and they haven't surfaced yet. But she's even harder to feed than Frank – there's no grace period, she just attacks me from the moment I open the cage door. I'll have to hide her medication and calcium supplements in the mince we're giving her.

The next step is to put Frank and Judy together – currently they're in separate cages – as a way of reducing the stress they're under. Only time will reverse the effect of the poisoning but if Frank's here and now Judy's here too, who's looking after the chicks?

Without at least one parent, the chicks will only survive six to twelve hours. They have to be fed constantly so they'd be very vulnerable with their food-gatherers gone.

I have no choice but to pay a visit to the Westfield tower and get them out of there.

44

The Will
to Live

A s Blackie is readied for surgery I prepare myself for it, too. Although I know Blackie is better off without his leg, amputation is not something I like to do, especially to such a young, vibrant cat.

Blackie has been a model patient: he lets us do what we need to do and doesn't fight us. Now, while I insert his catheter, he just looks up at me as if I'm his best friend in the world. I wonder if there's anything at all that upsets him – if having one leg not working at all and another leg badly banged up doesn't, what would?

Sara can't quite believe it, either.

'He has to be one of the most easy-going cats we've ever had in. Despite what we're doing to him he's still purring. He watches everything you do but everything's all right.'

My colleague Tony Mosman, who is the clinic's orthopaedic gun, will share the surgical duties with me, and he shaves

Blackie's left hind leg, which will be reconstructed. Then it's time for Sara to move Blackie onto the operating table. I will be amputating Blackie's right hind leg first and then Tony will perform the reconstruction on the left hind leg.

Although amputation probably sounds like a straightforward procedure, it's not. I have to be careful because there's a very big artery, vein and nerve involved. I have to find them, tie them off, make the cut and then get on with the business of removing the limb.

Tony is optimistic about the outcome for Blackie's badly damaged left leg: 'With cats' bones, someone once said that if you have one end of a bone and the other end of a bone in the same room, it will heal. Cats have remarkable recuperative powers with fractures.'

I look at the surgical instruments that Tony has laid out.

'Just your standard toolkit from the hardware store, Tony?'

'It is, a bit.' Tony then talks me through what he's doing. 'So what we're going to do here is put in a stainless wire to stop the leg rotating and then we put a small pin up the centre, which holds it in position.'

I'm still intrigued by his 'toolkit': 'You'd use the same tools at home to fix a broken chair or two. Plug them in and away you go,' I say, smiling.

'Tony did my cupboards as well,' says Sara. 'He did a really good job. They're still standing straight. It's looking good for you, Blackie.'

Tony inserts the pin. 'This pin now will drive up and stay there permanently. I don't think Blackie will have trouble with airport security – he's unlikely to be an international jetsetter.'

'But Blackie was telling me before,' I say, 'he's got big plans to go to Jamaica.'

After three hours in surgery, we're done; Tony and I are both happy with the results.

'The leg is now aligned as it should be,' says Tony, 'and it should have normal use of the knee joint again.' The knee joint is a little stiff as Tony tests it, but at least it's in the right groove.

It always seems incredible to finish an operation like that and think of it as the start of the journey, not the end, but in Blackie's case that's especially true: he has a big recovery ahead of him, and his success will depend on his mental and physical strength. With Blackie there's also the complicating factor that he now has only one hind leg, so the remaining left leg has to be 100 per cent straight as it will need to support his entire body weight. If that leg doesn't heal the way we hope, or if Blackie doesn't have the willpower to learn to live with and balance on three legs, there will be no future for him – there's the very real prospect that this surgery has just delayed the ending, not changed it.

Within twenty-four hours we'll have a good idea of whether he's going to get up and about easily.

* * *

The next morning Michael arrives at the clinic with his mother, Andrea. The family is Greek and Andrea has arrived bearing home-made delicacies for all of us.

'This is outrageous!' I exclaim when I see all the food. 'Hello, how are you? I'm Chris.'

'Nice to meet you,' says Andrea as she pats Blackie, who is clearly happy to see her.

'Blackie's looking about how I thought he would look,' I tell Andrea. 'He's lost a lot of blood in that surgery. He's lost a leg. And despite all the pain relief and anti-inflammatories, he's still feeling the effects of a big operation.

'It's obviously going to take a while for him to fully recover because he's lost such an important part of his body, plus he's had another operation at the same time – it's a double whammy. It's a really tough thing for him to get over. But he's just showing that Blackie spirit and he's fought on really hard.'

I can see Andrea looking at Blackie's reconstructed leg, and at the bald patch that has replaced his fur.

'The fur will grow back,' I reassure her. 'He won't have that Ugg boot on for the rest of his life.'

Earlier today I was worried about Andrea seeing Blackie with just three legs for the first time, and the big scar on the left hind leg. But she seems to be the toughie here – she barely flinched. It's clear that she loves her pet and the fact that he has three legs is not going to get in the way of her love for him.

'It's all right,' she tells me, 'because ten years ago my husband lost a finger. I go to the hospital – "Are you all right, Missus?" I'm all right.'

'She saw Dad have an accident at work,' Michael explains, 'and has witnessed these things before . . . She's a very tough lady.' Andrea then says something to Michael in Greek, and he translates for me. 'She's saying it's a shame, what happened to Blackie. He shouldn't have to go through this.'

I attempt to say some Greek to Andrea, to thank her for the food, but I think she's laughing at me . . . At any rate, the food looks amazing. What's also amazing is how Blackie's demeanour has changed since Andrea arrived. He reached out his little paws to greet her; now he's looking very relaxed. Because he's been through so much we keep forgetting he's just a kitten and, like any kitten, he has probably been missing his mum. Now he's seen her, this may be a defining point in his recovery.

However, that doesn't mean he can go home yet, no matter how much Andrea wants him to. Blackie needs to show me that he can walk first. In the meantime, I have to stop the rest of the staff eating the food before I get some . . .

There are yowls coming from the clinic's cattery, but none of them belong to Blackie. He's a model patient, still purring his way through his recovery.

'Isn't he the cutest cat you've ever seen?' Sara says when she goes to retrieve him for a check-up. 'After what he's been through . . . and he still likes us.' Sara is head over heels for

Blackie, and the rest of us are pretty fond of him too. Not only is he improving at a rapid rate but he's kept his good humour throughout. Even when I put my hands on his injured leg to check him over, he continues to purr.

There's a bit of swelling and quite a lot of bruising around the site of his surgery, and that's all to be expected. Now he needs some daily physiotherapy to keep his joints mobile. I start working his leg at the paw.

'No full-body massages here,' I tell him, 'or we'll have to get the aromatherapy oils out.'

Blackie seems to be enjoying the treatment, even without the smell of lavender, and while his hip joint is still inflamed, his knee joint is pretty good, all things considered. Both are working well enough for him to attempt to walk on them.

But before he can do that I need to rig up a support brace, and it has a very technical name: 'tea towel'. Sara is going to help me manoeuvre him to a standing position, but one look at her and Blackie is more interested in having a cuddle. I can see that the only way I'm going to motivate him to try is to threaten him with no more pats and cuddles till he walks. If only he could actually understand it when I tell him that.

'Come on, Blackie,' I urge him as he gingerly steps onto his paws. 'Come on, you're tougher than that.'

After a few attempts Blackie falls over with a thud, so with the next try I support most of his weight rather than making him bear it – I don't want him to go too hard, too fast and risk damaging his newly re-arranged knee joint, because that would be disastrous. It's better to slowly build up his muscles until they're ready to carry his body weight.

Part of the challenge is the fact that, for a little while, he'll still believe that his missing leg is there. His mind will need to adjust to his new situation and on a physical level he has to learn to adjust his balance and move his weight so he can anchor his back leg and then hop around.

A week after the operation, Blackie is not progressing as well as I'd like.

I suspect part of the problem is that he's being turned into a sook: the nurses love him, and if they all smother him with affection then he's going to think that all the rewards come without the need for hard work. You see, he's not just getting pats. He's also being carried around the clinic! I'm worried the nurses could be killing him with kindness.

I'm aware that his recovery is a complicated process – I can't see his muscles from the outside, so I can only go on what I can see of his function. He may still be in pain but, cats being stoic creatures, he's not going to show me that pain unless he's really suffering. So it's hard to truly assess what's going on. I don't want him to put too much pressure on the leg before it's ready, but I also don't want to baby him along and have the muscles and ligaments start to tighten up and fade away.

Sara is the main nurse in charge of Blackie's care; she's also the main nurse giving him all that love. Every time he does his exercises, instead of hopping up on his feet he just looks at her for a cuddle. I have to find a way to trick him to get onto his feet.

With Sara in the room, I prop Blackie onto his paws and then ask Sara to move away from him. Sure enough, Blackie wants to follow her – and he does it by walking. It's not a strong walk, but it's a walk. Once he collapses, exhausted, Sara rewards him with a pat.

We don't just want Blackie to walk around, though. We want him to *run* around, and to be so proficient on his legs that people are shocked when they realise he has only three of them. That's the goal.

Everyday we give Blackie physio and prompt him to walk and after two weeks of rehabilitation at the clinic, Blackie is ready to go home. After that initial reluctance to move on his own, he's made a truly incredible recovery and I'm really in awe of him. He's walking around brilliantly; he seems happy and I'm pretty sure he's ready to pick up his life where he left off.

'I'm thrilled,' says Michael when he comes to pick up his little mate. 'We're over the moon – this is awesome.'

'He's been so good,' I tell Michael.

I turn to give Blackie one last pat. 'I'll miss you around here but it's time to go home, mate. You stay out of trouble, Blackie.'

Although it's somewhat sad to see Blackie go, I have to remember that two weeks ago it looked like he was never going home. So my sadness is mixed with excitement for him and the great life he's going to have with such a loving family. No cat deserves it more. I feel really pleased to have been able to help get this lovely cat to this point but ultimately it is Blackie's will to live that led to his survival.

45

Free Flight

Bruce Campbell, the security manager at the Westfield shopping centre at Bondi Junction, escorts me to the top of the tower on the centre. I am really worried about the state I will find the chicks in and the only reassuring thought I have is that up here they're pretty safe from predators; no bird – no predator – goes near the peregrine falcon. They are the kings of the sky and every other animal respects them. They are the fastest, most lethal killing machine around so everyone else keeps their distance.

High above the shopping centre, Bruce points me in the right direction.

'All right, get over the edge,' he orders me.

'You'll be pleased to know I'm good with heights,' I reply before looking at what he's showing me. 'It's incredible – the peregrine falcon penthouse.'

The falcons have built their nest in the most secluded spot in Sydney – 200 metres above the ground and on a narrow ledge. We rig up a camera on a pole so we can move it closer to the falcons' nest. As it's in a precarious position, we don't want to take the risk of physically going there unless we're sure the chicks are alive. Hopefully the camera will get some vision of the nest and also deliver some good news about the chicks.

If the chicks are alive, we'll have to mount a rescue operation straightaway. One of the rigs used by the centre's window cleaners has been prepared for the job.

Bruce holds the pole camera and I watch on the monitor, giving him directions. I can see a lot of bird poo but no sign of life.

'Mate, I can't see anything moving,' I tell Bruce. The chicks are so small and vulnerable – it's possible that whatever is affecting Frank and Judy has struck them down too, or that time has simply been against them. Whatever the cause, there are no living chicks there for us to take back to Frank and Judy. And it's those two who have to be my priority from now on.

The good thing is that, once we get Frank and Judy back on their feet, they will be able to breed again. Falcons mate for life, so Frank and Judy are inseparable. They will always be together – so this is potentially a great love story of triumphing against the odds to start afresh. That's what I'd like to think, anyway – it will stop me feeling so disappointed about the chicks, who I just hope have already flown away to start their own new lives.

I don't have a lot of time to contemplate it, though – two different peregrine falcons have appeared and they do not like us intruding on Judy and Frank's nest. They start dive-bombing us and, not for the first time since I became a vet, I feel like I need danger money. And a helmet. Unfortunately there isn't one to hand, and I feel extremely vulnerable standing out in the open, 200 metres off the ground with the world's fastest animals circling overhead and trying to pick their moment.

'I can see one, but not the other one,' I say to Bruce. 'They're double-teaming into the sun and swooping. I really don't feel safe up here.' I duck as one of the falcons targets my head.

Once we remove ourselves from danger, Bruce tells me that he hopes Judy and Frank will be able to return to their 'peregrine penthouse' soon.

'It's a restricted area up there and the few of us who are fortunate enough to be allowed up to do our job marvel at the beauty of these birds. They're incredible . . . I'm a country boy and it's wonderful for me and a couple of the others who come from the bush to have the opportunity in the city – in the heart of the eastern suburbs – to see these magnificent creatures. So we've become very fond of them, are quite passionate and, right now, very concerned.'

The sincerity in Bruce's voice is unmistakeable and I assure him that things are looking good for Frank and Judy.

*   *   *

Two days after I return empty-handed from the tower, Judy and Frank are ready to be released. Frank's thrush has cleared up and both birds are far more robust than they were merely two days ago. A sure sign that any poison has now left their systems.

They are squawking in their cages, almost ready to burst out of them. I give Frank one last feed – they'll need the fuel if they're to fly home – and he's not nearly as easy to handle as he was that first day in the clinic. Now he seems to be quite edgy. It's a sign, though, that the time is right for releasing the pair.

We could kill these birds with kindness if we kept them in captivity too long. They'd become unfit and almost forget what is required to survive in the wild. And even though they're physically stronger, we need to find out if they still have the will to fly.

As I'm feeding them, I have no fear that they've forgotten how to use their equipment – one of Frank's talons is piercing my glove and, now, my finger. I think about the danger money again.

I take the falcons back to the shopping centre and Bruce escorts me to the tower. He is delighted that the birds have returned.

'It's awesome,' he says. 'Fantastic, mate.'

Frank and Judy are in their cages, ready to be sprung.

'Are we going to do it at the same time?' Bruce asks.

'One at a time,' I tell him. This is hopefully the moment they go back to being what they should be – wild birds cruising above Sydney. They must be itching to launch out of these boxes and get going.'

Frank is the first in line, so I grab him – although, unsurprisingly, he puts up a fight – and put him on the ledge. 'Recognise this, mate?' I ask him. 'See you later!'

But Frank isn't so willing to go. It's a nervous moment – for him, and for me – my heart starts thumping as I wonder what's going to happen. Frank takes a little practice leap onto the railing. He sits there, assessing the wind conditions, almost like a jet sitting at the end of the runway waiting for take-off clearance. Then he flaps his right wing and perks up considerably. Suddenly, he's off – soaring into the sky – and then just as suddenly he's swooped on by another falcon, so close that he's almost checking for ID – wanting evidence it is indeed Frank. It's not quite the perfect send-off I'd hoped for, but I'm happy nonetheless.

Now it's Judy's turn and, true to form, she's considerably more feisty than her mate. She flaps her wings as soon as she's out of the cage and then sits on the ledge for five minutes, with no sign of taking off.

'Come on, gorgeous,' I coax her, 'show us some wing.'

I doubt she's forgotten how to fly – her temporary paralysis is probably more due to the fact that there are strange human creatures standing around watching her. We back away a little.

This seems to do the trick – she's off into the air straight-away. It is truly a breathtaking sight – these perfectly engineered creatures that can be so graceful and yet so lethal. It is nature in motion, and I feel very lucky to be able to witness it from this rarefied vantage point.

Both Frank and Judy have passed this test beautifully. They could have dived down towards the ground but instead they fly up and away: all their instincts returned, their muscles stretched out and they just went for it.

'Mate, I'm absolutely stoked,' says Bruce. 'You've made my day, and all the security crew's and the cleaners'. It's absolutely awesome. You love them – we love them. It's absolutely fantastic.'

We're both disappointed about the chicks, but I'm confident that our peregrine pair will mate again next year.

Until then, they'll stalk the skies over Sydney, largely unnoticed by the humans below them. It's a good reminder for us all to pay more attention – to glance up occasionally, to look into trees and behind bushes – because our wildlife is all around. Whether we're in cities or rural areas, animals don't share our world – we share theirs.

Facts About the Peregrine Falcon

- Although the peregrine falcon is found across Australia, Europe, Asia, Africa and North and South America, it is not common to any of those continents.
- The peregrine falcon can live in most habitats, whether rainforest or desert, and at many altitudes. It chooses habitats that can provide large amounts of prey and where it can secure sites for nesting.
- The peregrine falcon feeds on small and medium-sized birds, rabbits and other mammals. It will hunt flying birds, as it can fly at speeds of up to 380 kilometres per hour, and it can soar to great heights.
- The falcon mates for life and the pairs maintain a 'sector' of twenty to thirty kilometres square throughout the year.
- The peregrine falcon does not build a nest but may take over the abandoned nest of another bird. Eggs may also be laid in recesses of cliff faces and tree hollows. While the female incubates the eggs the male brings her food, and once the eggs have hatched it is both parents who will hunt for food, usually cooperatively.

Source: www.birdsinbackyards.net/finder/display.cfm

46

Pet
Lover

The sunlight is glinting off the Bondi waves. It's a beautiful morning: the season has not quite turned towards summer, so there's still a bit of crispness in the air; little puffs of clouds appear here and there, but never enough to obscure the sun. This beach is a living organism – the ebb and flow of people along its boardwalks and the sand give it a rhythm that's almost like a heartbeat. I love it here; I never tire of looking at this beach, of living and working near it. Being able to spend so much of my life here and, through my work, to meet so many of the residents gives me a real sense of community. Bondi has its faults but they hardly matter in comparison to all it has to offer.

The waves are small today – not quite a metre high. Not really big enough for the regular surfers but certainly big enough for the hundreds of learners who splash and crash in among the foam.

It's lucky that there aren't many surfers out today. I won't be joining them, because I prefer a bigger wave. But the swell is just the right size for beginners of all shapes and sizes. And today that includes Rusty.

My faithful pet – my landlocked little kelpie – is today going to take to the waves for the first time in his life. I've never tried to teach a dog to surf before, and I'm not entirely convinced that Rusty is the right candidate. He's tentative at the best of times, so I can only guess at what he'll think about the surf. What looks like a small wave to me probably looks like a whole mountain of fear to him.

I've got him a soft board – the same type of board used in surf schools around Australia. It's long, which makes it more stable. For people learning to surf, it gives them a better opportunity to hop up to a standing position and stay there. For Rusty, it will provide more room for paws and claws to get a grip. And because it's not made of fibreglass it minimises the risk of anyone – human or dog – being injured by a whack to the head if they fall off.

I thought about looking for a doggie wetsuit – I'm sure they exist – but I don't think Rusty would go for it, even though the water is a bit chilly. He isn't carrying a lot of fat, nor is he covered in a big coat of fur, so for extra insurance against the elements I've got him his very own dog life jacket. It will keep him warm and afloat in the water!

You've probably seen some footage of surfing dogs – placid animals looking carefree as they coast into shore. This is not Rusty. The water isn't that deep – I can still stand – but it's deeper than anything he's used to, so I can understand why he's a bit nervous. On the other hand, some dogs are natural swimmers so he doesn't really have anything to worry about. Plus, growing up on a farm riding on the back of motorbikes has given Rusty an amazing sense of balance and self-belief. Surely this will be no different, right?

I study the waves rolling in as I hold Rusty's board. He will need a little wave with just the right amount of curl – no dumpers. I can't imagine how he'd react if he got dumped on his first-ever wave.

Early in the next set of waves, I spy just the right one making its way towards us.

'Are you ready, Rusty?' I say. He doesn't even turn his head. I'll take that as a 'yes'. I prop him up on all paws in preparation for his hang four.

As the wave crests behind me I give Rusty's board a push. It moves forward smoothly – not too quickly, just catching the wave nicely and heading for the beach . . .

Suddenly Rusty's no longer on the board. He's barely gone two metres and he's already abandoned ship. That's right – he jumped off, right into the wave. And in a no-nonsense way, paddles straight to shore.

'Rusty! RUSTY!'

I try to catch up to him but running in water isn't as easy for me as it is for him, and before I know it he's on the beach.

Rusty hits the sand running and takes off like a rocket. I'm not far behind him but his four legs and low centre of gravity outstrip my two legs and considerably greater height, and he's up the ramp to the car park before I'm even halfway up the beach.

'Rusty, come back! It wasn't that bad!'

Rusty tears along the footpath, heading for home. I trust him to be sensible around traffic, but I still want to catch up with him. Eventually he tires and I scoop him up. He's panting, and seems kind of annoyed with me. Or maybe with himself – it wasn't the most stellar surfing moment, after all.

I've accepted that Rusty is never going to share my love of surfing. He's a farm dog, after all – maybe he just doesn't understand the ocean or seem interested in his possible place in it. All I can do is give him a good life and keep him out of trouble – minus the odd surfing hiccup, of course.

I think that almost everyone who owns a pet feels that way about it. In my experience most pet owners love their animals a great deal and try their best to keep them healthy and provide them with fun, new experiences. In return they are given some of the greatest gifts of all: a devoted companion, unconditional love and, sometimes, a dedicated member of the family.

As inhabitants of a land with an extraordinary array of wildlife we also have a responsibility to make sure that our human lives do not unduly affect these animals. We've already taken over so many of their habitats – the least we can do is help them if they need it. So if you come across injured wildlife, contact your local vet or an organisation that can take care of the animal. And if you come across uninjured wildlife, don't do anything to change its status. I don't think it's asking too much to respect all animals the way they respect us. We can't expect humans to treat each other with kindness, dignity and compassion if we can't even treat animals that way.

The next time you're with your pet, or you see a wild animal either in its habitat or in a zoo, I hope you'll respect the fact that in many ways they are just like us – they have personalities, they often have emotions, and they can become sick or injured.

The world becomes so much wider and more interesting when you expand your point of view to include animals – there is so much beauty and grace to observe in them. They're not just little accessories or annoyances to feed; they don't just exist to pose in holiday photos at exotic locations. They are part of the global ecosystem, just as we are.

So the next time you take your dog for a walk, or you sit in your garden with your cat or pet rat or ferret, take the time to look around – at the trees, into the sky. Take the time to listen to the birdsong and, just maybe, the possum scratching on your roof. When you take this time, you'll realise that you don't just have one pet to look after: you're the part-time parent of a whole world of animals.

Contacts

Animal Welfare Organisations in Australia

Assistance Dogs Australia
A non-profit organisation committed to enhance the quality of life for people with physical disabilities.
1800 688 364
www.assistancedogs.org.au

Australian Registry of Wildlife Health
The Registry of Wildlife Health is a diagnostic and resource centre that focuses on detecting and diagnosing endemic, emerging and exotic diseases of wildlife that could have impacts on Australia's trade/economy, biodiversity, tourism and human health.
www.arwh.org

FAUNA (Foster care of Australia's Unique Animals Association Inc.)
A group of dedicated volunteer wildlife carers, who rescue and care for sick, injured or orphaned wildlife.
1300 FAUNA1 or 1300 328 621
www.fauna.com.au

Guide Dogs Australia
A non-profit brand that represents all of Australia's state-based Guide Dog organisations, assisting people who are blind or have a vision impairment in gaining the freedom and independence to move safely and confidently around the community and to fulfil their potential.
1800 804 805
www.guidedogsaustralia.com

National Parks and Wildlife Service: Australian Capital Territory
www.atn.com.au/parks/contact

National Parks and Wildlife Service: New South Wales
www.environment.nsw.gov.au/nationalparks

National Parks and Wildlife Service: South Australia
www.environment.sa.gov.au/parks

National Parks and Wildlife Service: Western Australia
08 9474 9055
www.calm.wa.gov.au/national_parks

National Parks and Wildlife Service: Northern Territory
08 8999 4555
www.nt.gov.au/nreta/parks

National Parks and Wildlife Service: Tasmania
1300 135 513
www.parks.tas.gov.au

RSPCA (Royal Society for the Prevention of Cruelty to Animals)
An international organisation that works towards preventing cruelty to animals by actively promoting their care and protection.
02 6282 8300
www.rspca.org.au

SASH (Small Animal Specialist Hospital)
A referral hospital based in Sydney, this hospital has a team of dedicated specialists that work together to provide high-quality and compassionate care for pets and also provides 24-hour emergency and critical care.
02 9889 0289
www.sashvets.com

Sydney Wildlife (Sydney Metropolitan Wildlife Services)
A volunteer organisation that is dedicated to caring for Sydney's sick, injured or orphaned native fauna.
02 9413 4300
www.sydneywildlife.org.au

Taronga Conservation Society Australia

A national society responsible for the operation of Taronga and Taronga Western Plains Zoos that is recognised by the World Conservation Organisation as a leader in the world zoological community. Its primary objectives are to facilitate visitor and community education, biological research and wildlife conservation and to maximise the visitor experience by providing a unique and exciting educational tour of each zoo with animals exhibited in an environment similar to their natural habitat.
02 9969 2777

www.taronga.org.au

Taronga Western Plains Zoo

A world-renowned centre for its care of wildlife, breeding programs (especially of endangered species), conservation programs, education facilities and exhibits, this zoo is now widely recognised as Australia's greatest open plain zoo. It is also an education centre, a research centre and a wildlife conservation and preservation centre for species from all over the world.
02 6881 1400

www.taronga.org.au/western-plains-zoo

Taronga Zoo

The Taronga Foundation works towards the development of philanthropic support for the conservation and preservation of Australian and exotic wildlife.
02 9969 2777

www.taronga.org.au

WIRES (Wildlife Information Rescue & Education Service Inc.)
Rescue call centre: 13000 WIRES or 1300 094 737
www.wires.org.au

Acknowledgments

Dr Chris Brown: Thank you to all the staff at Bondi Junction Veterinary Hospital: Julia, Tony, Neil, Sara, Mel, Liesel, Jules, Lee, Kelly, Laura, Jill, Suze.

Thanks to Dr Lisa Chimes.

Thank you to the crew who worked on the series: Daryl, Steve, Sparky, Lawso, Janey, Kate, Bozo, Paul, Tanya, Tamara, Cathy, Dave, John, Steve. Thanks also to David, Daffyd and Cat from Network Ten. And finally thanks to my flatmates Brad, Perko, Simon and Candice for putting up with both me and my occasional houseguests.

Anna Hille: Thanks to Dr Lisa Chimes for her assistance with this book; Daryl Talbot, Tania Nesbit and all at WTFN; our publisher, Vanessa Radnidge, and the sales, publicity and marketing departments at Hachette Australia; all the staff of the Bondi Junction Veterinary Hospital; and, of course, the animals and owners who have shared their stories. Special thanks to Robbie, David, Nick and Judy.